Bohumil S D...

THE CYTOLOGY AND LIFE-HISTORY OF BACTERIA

THE CYTOLOGY AND LIFE-HISTORY OF BACTERIA

BY

K. A. BISSET, D.Sc.

Reader in Systematic Bacteriology,
University of Birmingham

SECOND EDITION

E. & S. LIVINGSTONE, LTD.

EDINBURGH AND LONDON

1955

Acknowledgements

I WISH to acknowledge with gratitude the assistance given to me in the production of this book by the Editors of the *Journal of Hygiene*, the *Journal of General Microbiology*, the *Journal of Pathology and Bacteriology*, *Experimental Cell Research*, and *Biochimica et Biophysica Acta*, all of whom lent blocks of illustrations ; by the *Cambridge University Press, Oliver & Boyd Ltd.*, and the *Elsevier Press* who provided the blocks in question, and especially by Dr. Emmy Klieneberger-Nobel, Dr. Woutera van Iterson, Professor J. Tomcsik, Dr. A. L. Houwink and Drs. Birch-Anderson, Maaløe and Sjöstrand, whose admirable micrographs are the subject of many of these illustrations.

I wish also to thank the Editors of the *Proceedings of the Royal Society*, the *Journal of Bacteriology*, the *Annales de l'Institut Pasteur*, the *Proceedings of the Society for Experimental Biology and Medicine* and *Cold Spring Harbor Symposia*, Professor R. H. Stoughton, Professor R. J. V. Pulvertaft, Dr. J. Lederberg, Dr. R. R. Mellon, Dr. E. O. Morris, Professor A. R. Prévot and Drs. Chapman and Hillier for permission to reproduce illustrations, and Dr. Joyce Grace, Miss P. E. Pease, Miss B. G. Fewins and Mr A. A. Tuffery for their helpful observations and material.

Lastly, I wish to thank Professor J. F. D. Shrewsbury for the facilities which he has placed at my disposal ; and Miss C. M. F. Hale for her skilled and patient work in the preparation of the cytological material upon which this monograph is based.

K. A. BISSET,
Department of Bacteriology,
University of Birmingham.

Preface to Second Edition

THE second edition of this monograph includes a considerable amount of new information which serves, for the most part, to confirm and expand the general theories of cytological structure and behaviour in bacteria which I advanced six years ago. In particular, greatly improved demonstrations have been achieved of such, formerly rather problematical processes as gonidial reproduction, nuclear reduction, and the development of the flagella, and of such structures as the blepharoplast or the startlingly complex cross-walls which sub-divide a staphylococcus internally.

I have continued to place the main weight of my arguments upon my own observations or upon information which I have been able personally to confirm, but have welcomed several remarkable contributions to knowledge in the form, for example, of Chapman and Hillier's electron micrographs of sections of *Bacillus cereus*, which prove, contrary to my previous belief, that the cross-wall is indeed a centripetal ingrowth, and the consummately skilful phase contrast studies of Tomcsik which, while demonstrating the profundity of my former ignorance of the nature of bacterial capsules, provide a gratifying confirmation of my hypothesis, based upon entirely different evidence, of the development of cell wall.

Since the first edition was published there has also been a notable increase in the amount of corroborative evidence provided by studies in genetics, biochemistry and biophysics. The single, reductionally dividing chromosome of the vegetative nucleus, which has been the subject of the most lucid cytological demonstrations, has been entirely vindicated by the genetical studies of Witkin and of Cavalli-Sforza and Jinks, after a period in which multiple, or even branched chromosomes, for the existence of which there is no acceptable cytological evidence, were at various times postulated by geneticists. And in a similar manner, the cytological and physico-chemical evidence upon the behaviour of cell envelopes and flagella have been in exceedingly close accordance, and have even begun to shed some light upon the problems of antigenic structure.

Since it is now the subject of a separate monograph (*Bacteria*, Livingstone), the chapter upon bacterial systematics has been omitted, but the allied problem, more cogent to this study, of cytological evidence of the evolutionary relationships of bacteria, has been discussed at greater length.

Because the text is intended to be a synthesis of available information, the practice of relegating references to the head of each sub-section, except in cases of argument or of historical interest, has been continued. There appears to be a consensus of agreement that what may be lost in ease of tracing a reference to a single point is more than gained in clarity and brevity.

April 1955   K. A. BISSET.

Preface to First Edition

THIS book does not attempt to review the literature upon bacterial cytology, of which the bulk is very great and the value, in many cases, difficult to assess. The bibliography is confined to a relatively small number of works, almost all recent. No attempt has been made to supply references for analytical discussion or general information.

The purpose is rather to present a reasoned case for regarding bacteria as living cells with the same structure and functions as other living cells, and to correlate the available information upon the various types of bacteria.

Bacteria, as living creatures, have been little studied. It is their activities as biochemical or pathological agents which have received almost undivided attention. Even these problems, however, cannot fail to be clarified by a better knowledge of the organisms responsible.

It is also hoped that biological workers in other fields may profit by contact with this, largely unknown, body of evidence, and may find the comparisons and analogies useful and stimulating in their related studies.

I have attempted, as far as possible, to base my arguments upon my own observations, or upon such information as I have been able personally to confirm. Where I have not had the opportunity to do so, I have tried to indicate clearly the status of the argument.

K. A. B.

December 1949

Contents

List of Illustrations

CHAPTER I

Introduction

MUCH of what has in the past been written of the morphology of bacteria has been based upon the assumption that, because of their small size, and the difficulty, by the methods usually employed, of observing the complexities of their structure, they may be regarded as simple in form and primitive in philogeny.

The temptation to regard small size, and simplicity of structure, whether real or apparent, as criteria of a primitive condition, has often proved the cause of error and confusion in the classification of other groups of living organisms. As more information becomes available it is almost invariably discovered that the simplest creatures exhibit characters which suggest a relationship with others, much more complex, or may themselves prove to be less simple than they had been believed. This has proved to be true of bacteria also. Although for long believed, in spite of much evidence to the contrary, to be almost structureless cells, reproducing by simple fission, they have proved to possess an intricacy of structure rivalling that of any other type of living cell, and to undergo life-cycles of considerable complexity.

There is little doubt that the reason why so much more has been learned of the physiology of bacteria than of their morphology, is their very great importance in medicine, industry and agriculture. The immediate, practical problems of bacteriology have overshadowed the more academic questions of their biological nature. The techniques which were devised for the solution of these problems have been notable, in almost every case, for their failure to provide even a minimum of basic, biological information. Indeed it may be said that much of the information of this nature, accumulated since the commencement of systematic bacteriology, has tended rather to obscure than to clarify the underlying truths.

Especially is this true of the staining techniques employed for routine

A

examination of bacteriological material and cultures. The distorted vestiges of bacteria which survived the technique of drying and heat-fixation were accepted as truly indicative of the morphology of the living organisms. And while, from time to time, satisfaction has been expressed at the fact that bacteria will survive, undistorted, treatment which produces the most obvious damage in larger cells, the validity of the assumption that they do, in fact, survive such treatment has seldom been called to question.

Staining methods have also been devised, almost without exception, for the purpose of identifying clinically important species of bacteria, and are often most admirably suited to this task. It is surprising to find, however, that much time and labour has been directed to the elucidation of the appearances observed by these methods, and the explanation, in cytological terms, of the artefacts which they produce.

Even with this disability a great deal of accurate information has in fact been obtained, but has failed to carry conviction. In many cases this has been because of inadequate illustration, which alone can make such studies comprehensible, except to the initiate. Probably the reason has been an unduly pessimistic view of the possibilities of photomicrography, and a certain timidity in the submission of drawings and diagrams, due perhaps to a fear of misinterpreting such tiny structures, and a corresponding fear of ridicule.

It is also remarkable that many workers in the field of bacterial cytology appear to have been almost entirely ignorant of the parallel studies of others, and have failed to receive the stimulus which such knowledge can afford. Conversely, there has been no lack of reviews of the subject, but these have often been made by authors whose lack of practical knowledge of the structures described has disqualified them for the task of correlating the available information, which is often obscure and mutually contradictory.

The artificiality of contemporary or recent views upon bacterial morphology has thus served to widen the gap between bacteriology and other biological sciences, as well as to confuse and retard the advance of bacteriology itself.

In the evolution of modern cytological methods, much is owed to the interest taken by mycologists in the myxobacteria. These micro-organisms do not respond well to the techniques of heat-fixation and Gram's stain, most usually employed in routine bacteriology, and the necessity for the employ-ment of more refined methods of examination has encouraged the study of eubacteria in a similar manner. The readily-demonstrable nuclear structures and beautiful and complex life-cycle of myxobacteria stimulated the search for the truth concerning the parallel structures and processes in those bacterial genera more commonly encountered in the laboratory.

The studies of biochemists upon the nucleoproteins of bacteria have also contributed greatly to the increase in our knowledge of, and interest in, the problems of bacterial cytology. One of the most useful staining techniques for the demonstration of the bacterial nucleus is a direct adaptation of a microchemical test, the Feulgen reaction, which has itself given much information upon the subject.

Bacteria have recently come to be regarded as suitable material for genetical studies, and although little has so far been done to correlate genetical and cytological information, a gratifying degree of mutual support has already been achieved (Chapter X), and it is to be hoped that the interchange of information between these two branches of bacteriology may, in the future, prove as helpful to both as it has done in other biological fields.

The information compiled in the following chapters has been obtained by classical microscopic methods, in most instances, but a considerable advance in the techniques of electron and phase-contrast microscopy, as applied to this subject, has in the last few years provided valuable confirmatory evidence on several points, and promises to do more. It should be emphasised that a reasonable degree of correlation between the results obtainable by different techniques must always be sought before too much weight is placed upon any one of these. The disagreements which have arisen in bacterial cytology have been surprisingly few. But almost all of these have been caused by the uncritical reliance of a single worker, or a small group, upon a single method.

CHAPTER II

Technique

THE progress of our knowledge of bacterial morphology has, in the past, been considerably retarded by the fact, which may at first have appeared advantageous, that recognisable microscopic preparations of bacteria can be made by the technique of the heat-fixed film. A small quantity of a bacterial culture, or of pus, or similar pathological material, is thinly spread upon a slide, dried, and then heated strongly with a naked flame, in order to fix it firmly upon the slide. Bacteria fixed in this manner and stained by Gram's method, or simply with a strong solution of a basic dye, dried once more and examined directly under the oil-immersion lens of the microscope (the oil serving also as a clearing agent), preserve an appearance which enables them to be recognised as bacteria, and even classified within rather broad limits. Their appearance under this treatment has become familiar to generations of bacteriologists, and is usually that which is recorded in the descriptions of species. Little or no detail can be perceived in such a preparation, and it has thus become, and until recently has remained a dogma that no detail exists to be seen. This opinion is fortified by the fact that equally little structure can, as a rule, be made out in unstained, living bacteria, especially as these are seldom at rest, either because of their own motility or from the effect of Brownian movement.

It is true that, from time to time, valuable observations upon the structure of bacteria have been made, either by the cytological techniques already employed in other biological sciences, or by a careful study of unstained material, but little attention has been paid to these findings by the great majority of bacteriologists, and the interpretation of heat-fixed material has not been questioned seriously.

The main reason for the uniform appearance of stained bacteria is that their affinity for the basic dyes which are commonly employed is so great that the strongly stained cytoplasm and cell membranes mask the underlying structures. This masking effect is accentuated by the shrinkage which results from drying. This shrinkage is often very considerable, reducing the bacterium to as little as half or a third of its natural size, and manifesting itself typically in the appearance of the anthrax bacillus or of related chain-forming bacilli,

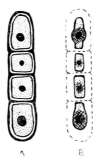

(Reproduced from the Journal of General Microbiology)

Fig. 1.

THE MORPHOLOGY OF *C. DIPHTHERIAE.*

A. True morphology.
B. " Typical appearance " in heat-fixed material. The cell
    contents are shrunken and the cell wall unstained.

in which considerable gaps are seen between the visible bacilli, actually the shrunken protoplasts. The rigid cell wall remains unstained and invisible, holding the chain together. Drying and shrinkage are an essential part of many staining procedures, notably those intended to demonstrate the " typical morphology " of *Corynebacterium diphtheriæ*. The metachromatic granules cannot be demonstrated in undried preparations, and are, in fact, artefacts produced by the specific staining of a dried aggregate of nuclear and other basophilic material.

Many bacteria are multicellular, and their appearance is much altered by drying. The granular appearance of the tubercle bacillus is due to the shrinkage of the contents of the small, almost spherical cells which make up the bacillus, so that unstained gaps appear between them. In this case also the cell wall remains unstained, but retains the dried cells in their original relationship.

It will thus be seen that three main problems must be solved in the demonstration of the true morphology of bacteria. Distortion due to drying must be avoided, the masking effect of the strongly staining protoplasm and cell membranes overcome, and those structures demonstrated which, like the cell wall, are difficult to stain. The first is simple and entails merely the avoidance of drying at all stages of preparation. The second and third present more difficulty. The problem of overcoming the masking effect of the surface structures was solved, as so often happens, by accident.

B: HYDROLYSIS TECHNIQUES FOR NUCLEAR STAINING
(13, 15, 16, 19, 24, 30, 32, 40, 41, 44, 46, 48, 50, 51, 52, 53, 57)

The Feulgen reaction is a microchemical test which depends upon the formation of a purple compound when aldehydes react with Schiff's reagent. A positive Feulgen reaction is given by deoxyribose nucleic acid, after its purine bases have been removed by acid hydrolysis. Ribonucleic acid does not give a positive reaction. The hydrolysis is performed in Normal hydrochloric acid at a temperature of 60° C., and the subsequent staining with Schiff's reagent reveals the nuclear structures of bacteria with reasonable clarity. This was one of the first methods to give a true picture of the bacterial nucleus, and it was later discovered that if the final staining was performed with Giemsa's solution, instead of Schiff's reagent, a much clearer picture was obtained. This was the acid-Giemsa stain, which has been the basis of nearly all recent work upon the bacterial nucleus, although the information which it provides can be verified by other methods.

The purpose of the preliminary treatment with hydrochloric acid is two-fold. The nucleoproteins of the underlying structures are partially hydrolysed so that the aldehyde group of the associated pentose sugar is released and combines with the staining agent. At the same time the stainable material of the outer layers of the cell is more completely hydrolysed, so that its masking effect is reduced. This differentiation is made possible by the fact that the nuclear structures are composed largely of Feulgen-positive deoxyribose nucleoproteins, whereas the cell membrane and surface layers of the cytoplasm usually contain a higher proportion of ribose nucleoproteins.

To perform the stain, smear preparations are made upon slides or cover-slips. They may be unfixed, although these tend to wash off, or they may be fixed in osmic acid vapour. Most fixatives should be avoided as they may completely alter the appearance of the nucleus.

Hydrolysis in Normal HCl should be conducted at a temperature, approximately, of 60° C. Staining, in dilute Giemsa, is best performed at 37° C.

The periods required for hydrolysis and staining are exceedingly variable and may be different at different ages of the same culture. It is often necessary to examine the preparation with the microscope, in order to determine whether it is suitably stained, and for this purpose a water-immersion lens is a great convenience. Most bacteria require from ten to twenty minutes hydrolysis, and thirty minutes in the staining solution. Some require longer periods or stronger solutions.

A properly stained preparation is bright pink in colour, the nuclear structures staining more intensely than the cytoplasm, which may stain bluish or purple in some cases. Inadequate hydrolysis is indicated by a uniform purple colour, and excessive hydrolysis by a pale pink colour and blurred outline. Inadequate or excessive staining periods are self-evident in the appearance of the preparation.

It is important to use fresh reagents, and otherwise inexplicable failures may be found to be due to neglect to do so.

Other methods of staining give comparable results, and may be useful in the case of bacteria which do not stain well by the classical method. Cold perchloric or trichloracetic acid, or even weak alkalis, may be substituted for hydrochloric acid. A variety of different dyes may be used instead of Giemsa. Thionin gives good results and has been widely used, but is much less specific than Giemsa, and stains the basophilic elements of the cell envelopes as well as the nucleus, which is liable to cause confusion in interpretation.

C: DIFFERENTIATION TECHNIQUES

(2, 10, 13, 20, 48, 66)

The methylene-blue-eosin method has been used to demonstrate the nuclear material of bacteria which will not stain readily by acid–Giemsa, it is unfortunately irregular in its results and may be liable to produce artefacts.

Basically the method is exceedingly simple. The preparation is stained with aqueous methylene blue and differentiated with eosin. The cytoplasm stains pale blue, and the nuclear structures dark blue or purple. In practice, however, it is a difficult technique to perform, and is not suitable for all strains of bacteria.

The film should be made thick and stained until dark blue throughout. It is then washed in water, differentiated for a few seconds in eosin and immediately washed again. The action of the eosin is very rapid, and it will entirely remove the blue colour if it is allowed to act for too long.

It was noted previously that this technique may usefully be employed upon bacteria which resist staining by acid–Giemsa, and the converse is also true. For this reason, methylene-blue-eosin is best regarded as a useful adjunct to acid-Giemsa, and is not recommended as a routine cytological method.

Similar results are obtainable by the use of crystal violet, with nigrosin as a differentiating agent.

D: THE ROMANOWSKY STAINS

(36, 47)

The methylene-blue-eosin technique differs from the better-known staining methods of the Romanowsky type in that the combination of the acidic and basic dyes is permitted to take place during the period of the staining reaction. The more orthodox methods are often of considerable value, however, and simple staining with Giemsa will often prove of value in the case of bacteria, such as myxobacteria and some members of other orders, whose surface structures lack the strong affinity for dyes exhibited by many. Valuable observations have been made in a variety of bacterial groups by the use of these methods.

E: SIMPLE DYES
(1, 14, 58, 59)

Even the simple dyes, especially basic fuchsin and methylene blue, may be of value upon occasion, if the errors of heat-fixation and drying, which usually accompany their use, can be avoided. The affinity of bacterial cytoplasm for the basic dyes is so great that a short treatment will often produce an appearance of negative staining of the nuclear structures, which appear pale and refractive against the stained background. This phenomenon is well known, and is usually described as bipolar staining. Accumulations of basophilic material at the poles are also associated with the growth of the cell. Reagents and even displaced nucleic acids may form aggregates in these areas and appear as granular artefacts.

An interesting refinement in the use of a simple dye, which has been employed with considerable success, consists in permitting a thin film of carbol fuchsin to dry upon a slide. The bacteria are suspended in a drop of water upon the coverslip which is inverted upon the slide and sealed at the edges. The dye is taken up gradually by the bacteria and the process may be followed under the microscope.

This method has proved of value in the description of certain of the complex processes which precede the formation of the resting nucleus, but appears to have failed to demonstrate the active, vegetative condition of the nucleus in the same species of bacteria.

F: THE USE OF PROTEIN MATERIALS
(17, 25, 60, 61, 62, 63, 64, 65, 68)

As the surface material, the affinity of which for basic dyes tends to obscure the internal structures of bacteria, is composed mainly of ribose nucleic acid, it has been found possible to digest away this material with the enzyme ribonuclease. This leaves unharmed the deoxyribose nucleic acids of the nucleus itself, which can then be demonstrated without difficulty.

Valuable results have been achieved by the digestion of surface structures with lysozyme and by various combinations of lysozyme, trypsin and other proteins at specific values of pH, and by phase-contrast studies of the effects upon the cell of antibodies active against cell-envelope components. (Section L, below.)

G: CLASSICAL CYTOLOGICAL PROCEDURES
(3, 11, 14, 18, 43, 51, 67)

The cytological staining techniques which have been employed for plant or animal cells are often of value also in the case of bacteria. These are too numerous to be dealt with in detail.

Iron alum hæmatoxylin and borax carmine have both proved useful in demonstrating the bacterial nucleus.

Cytochemical techniques for the demonstration of polysaccharide food reserves, fat globules and similar materials have been extensively utilised in the investigation of bacteria, but the results achieved have been marred by the absence of any attempt, in most cases, to preserve the natural appearance of the cells. It is also the opinion of the author that these supposedly specific staining reactions, of which the use of osmic acid vapour or the naphthol dyes for lipids are fair examples, are much less reliable than has been supposed.

The enigmatic nature of the majority of demonstrable granules in bacteria is tacitly admitted by the practice of coining for them such titles as " meta-chromatic granules " or " volutin " ; they have even been claimed to be mitochondria. These granules are rarely apparent except in dried material, and are often artefacts, although it is not denied that reserve foodstuffs, in the form of polysaccharides or lipids, may normally be present in the bacterial cell. It is also beyond question that the nuclear bodies of bacteria have many times been described in circumstances which have led to their being confused with these and other unidentifiable granules.

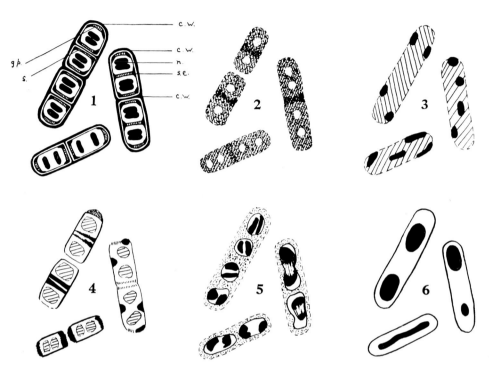

(Reproduced from Experimental Cell Research)

FIG. 2

A GROUP OF *BACILLUS* FIXED AND STAINED BY VARIOUS METHODS

(1) Diagram of the cytological structure of a group of bacilli at various stages of cell division. The top-left bacillus is divided into four cells by complete cross-walls ; fission is commencing. The top-right bacillus is divided by a complete cross-wall and subdivided by cytoplasmic septa alone. The lower bacillus has recently divided and has only two cells. *c.w.*, cell wall ; *g.p.*, growing point ; *s.*, cytoplasmic septum preceding cross-wall ; *s.e.*, septum in early stage ; the darkly-stained junctions of the septa are growing points ; *n*, nucleus.

(2) The same group demonstrated by a simple, basic dye.

(3) Stained by Gram and over decolorised.

(4, 5) Artefacts caused by unsuitable fixation.

(6) Sporulation appearances.

H: CELL WALL STAINS

(8, 9, 16, 18, 20, 26, 27, 28, 37, 38, 39, 45, 53, 56, 66)

Bacteria are enclosed in a rigid cell wall which normally resists staining. It may be rendered visible by mordanting in tannic acid, phosphomolybdic acid or cationic detergents. These agents serve the dual purpose of mordanting the cell wall and so altering the protein material of the cell that it is rendered unstainable and does not obscure the details of the transverse septa, where these occur. Tannic acid also forms a stainable complex upon the surface of the cell wall, and if it is stained before the mordanting process is complete, this complex may produce an outline picture of the wall, but fail to show internal details. Using 5-10% tannic acid, the wall can be stained with 0·2% crystal violet ; with 1% phosphomolybdic acid, 1% methyl green gives the clearest results. The times required for staining and mordanting vary from a few seconds upwards.

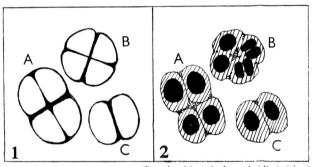

(Reproduced from the Journal of Bacteriology)

Fig. 3

THE CYTOLOGICAL STAINING OF COCCI

(1) *Micrococcus cryophilus* by Hale's method for cell walls. Showing two- or four-celled cocci.

(2) A similar group stained by trichloracetic acid and Giemsa. Such arrangements of nuclear material have been misconstrued as mitotic figures by some observers.

The underlying cell membrane is not easily demonstrated. Transverse septa derived from it, containing a large protein component, are stainable by simple, basic dyes or by acid-Giemsa, and are sometimes rendered more obvious by fixation with Bouin's solution or similar agents. Bacteria which have been slightly plasmolysed by such fixatives can be stained by 0·05% Victoria blue in such a manner as to demonstrate the cell wall and cell membrane simultaneously.

Bacterial cell membranes are also stained by dyes of the Sudan, fat soluble group. This probably indicates the presence of a lipoid or lipoprotein component, which is also believed to exist in the cell membranes of other organisms, but probably does not mean that the cell membrane should be regarded as predominantly lipoid in constitution.

In addition to the well-known methods of Hiss's and Muir's stains, capsules and slime layers are also stainable by the tannic-acid-violet technique, but these methods give little hint of the remarkable structure which can be discerned in bacterial capsules by phase-contrast microscopy.

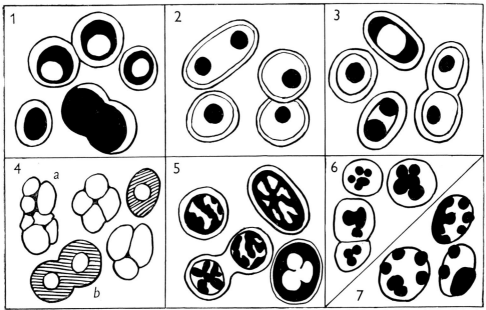

(Reproduced from the Journal of General Microbiology)

FIG. 4

CYTOLOGICAL STAINING OF AZOTOBACTER

Appearances produced by various staining tecnhiques.

(1) Nucleated cells stained by lithium carbonate and Giemsa.

(2) As (1), by magnesium sulphate and thionin.

(3) As (1), by nitric acid and thionin.

Comparison of these figures shows positive and negative differential staining of the large perinuclear granules.

(4) Phase-contrast studies of *a*, vacuolated and *b*, nucleated cells.

(5) Vacuolated cells by nitric acid and thionin. The outlines of the lipid globules alone are stained.

(6, 7) As (5), stained for lipids by Ziehl-Neelsen and Sudan IV. respectively. In the latter case the lipids have become displaced towards the periphery; possibly because of partial solution.

I: THE MOUNTING OF MATERIAL

(8, 9, 10, 11, 12, 22, 24, 29, 42, 53)

Cytological preparations should be mounted upon the thinnest available slides and coverslips, and it is a distinct advantage to prepare the smear upon the coverslip, so that the part of the preparation which is firmly adherent to the glass is nearest to the objective of the microscope. It is also simpler to transfer a coverslip from one reagent to another without the necessity of employing large volumes of fluid. The author has found sputum tubes and watchglasses to be very suitable as containers, and the small volumes of reagents which they contain may be renewed at frequent intervals.

Coverslips should be sealed to the slide, at the edges, with wax or vaseline, unless the preparations are dehydrated and mounted, to which there is no theoretical objection. In practice, however, it will be found that some shrinkage and distortion will usually result, and the clarity of the finished preparation will compare unfavourably with that of a simple water mount, although possessing the advantage of being permanent. If the edges are carefully sealed a water mounted preparation will last for several days, in the refrigerator, although it may deteriorate rapidly at room temperature.

It is worth emphasising that far more detail can usually be made out in a good photomicrograph, with all the advantages of colour filtration, than can be discerned, by the most experienced observer, by direct microscopic examination. Impermanence of preparations is thus of little importance provided that interesting appearances are photographed. It is also true that appearances which cannot be reproduced, more or less at will, are unlikely to be either true or important, and their impermanence is not to be regretted.

FIG. 5

BASOPHILIC GRANULES IN THE CELL ENVELOPES OF *BACILLUS*

(1, 2) Partially acid-hydrolysed bacteria, stained with Giemsa, showing nuclear bodies and granula and diffuse basophilia respectively in the cell envelopes.

(3) Over-hydrolysed specimens showing occasional granules.

(4, 5, 6) As (3) with added, extraneous DNA which has adhered in the form of stainable granules, especially at the poles and cross-walls. This indicates that the granules appearing naturally in (1) and (3) may well consist of similar nucleic acids translated from the nucleus and cell envelopes by the hydrolysis procedure. Such granules have frequently been misinterpreted as nuclear bodies, mitotic centrioles, mitochondria, etc., etc.

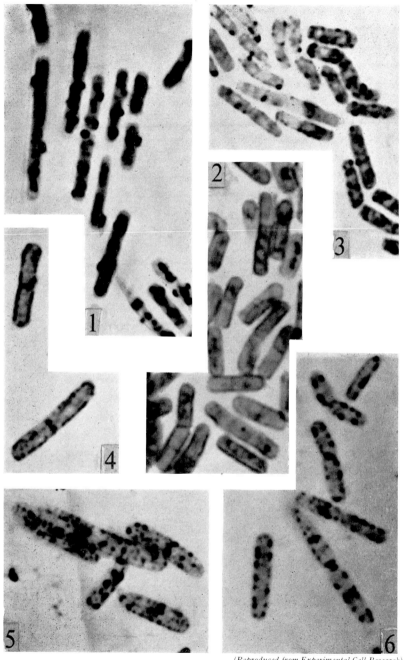

(Reproduced from Experimental Cell Research)

FIG. 5

J: THE STAINING OF FLAGELLA

The classical methods for the demonstration of flagella may be obtained from any elementary text-book upon practical bacteriology. Flagella are too small to be resolved by visible light although their presence can be determined by dark-ground illumination or phase-contrast microscopy. Their staining depends upon the aggregation of solid material upon their surface, to increase their apparent size. These methods are of little or no cytological value, and are not entirely to be relied upon, even for information upon the presence or absence of flagella, or upon their arrangement, as they have, in the past, given contradictory evidence upon these points.

K: ELECTRON MICROSCOPY

(4, 21, 30, 33, 34, 35, 49, 54, 55)

The electron microscope suffers from two defects in its application to biological materials ; the specimen to be examined must be completely desiccated before introduction into the vacuum chamber, and the penetration of the electron beam is so low that only the thinnest specimens can be properly defined. For these reasons, until recently the most valuable contribution of the electron microscope to bacterial cytology was in the study of flagella. In the last few years, however, valuable studies have been made of cell envelopes in disrupted bacteria, and even more promising has been the development of techniques which enable ultra-thin sections of bacteria to be cut and examined by the electron microscope. The electron beam has also been put to a slightly different purpose in the study of diffraction patterns produced by the cell walls of bacteria and other micro-organisms.

The scope of this section does not permit a detailed description of the techniques of electron microscopy, upon which several complete books have been written, but a number of examples are included among the illustrations of the types of information which can be obtained from this source.

At the same time, some comments upon the sectioning of bacteria may be of value. In the opinion of the author, although the technical problems of obtaining electron-transparent sections have been solved, that of embedding the material and fixing or otherwise treating it so as to obtain reasonable contrast between the internal structures, without gravely compromising the validity of the appearances to be interpreted, has not been solved. The use of strong solutions of heavy metals (nearly all of which are active protein precipitants) as "stains" to increase contrast, is especially open to criticism, if the appearance of such tiny structures is to be taken at its face value.

Sections of bacteria prepared in this laboratory and accorded minimal treatment show very poor internal contrast, but the form of such nuclear structures as are visible accords quite closely with what can be seen in stained preparations. This is not the case with osmium-treated material.

Any mechanically sound microtome can be adapted, by gearing-down, to thin sectioning. Methacrylate resin is widely employed for embedding purposes, but polystyrenes have been used with success in this laboratory, and a very wide range of comparable materials is available.

L: PHASE-CONTRAST MICROSCOPY
(15, 23, 60, 61, 62, 63, 64)

By the use of the phase-contrast microscope it has been possible to confirm upon living bacteria the main outlines of the nuclear cycle observable in fixed, stained material. In such untreated material, however, the clarity of the observations leaves much to be desired, and little or no information is obtainable upon those structures which do not differ from their surroundings in refractive index.

A revolution in the use of the phase-contrast microscope, comparable with the introduction of specific staining methods in classical microscopy, has resulted from the brilliant work of Tomcsik, who, by the use of enzymes, antibodies and other proteins has specifically demonstrated a variety of chemically definable materials and structures in the bacterial cell, and has revealed an entirely unsuspected complexity of structural detail in the capsule.

The most striking of Tomcsik's methods, which is possibly the greatest single advance in cytochemical technique in the last half-century, and which has potential applications in all biological fields, consists in the preparation of

B

antibodies against chemically defined fractions of (*e.g.*) the bacterial capsule. When these antibodies are allowed to react with bacteria which contain the appropriate chemical fraction, in the field of the phase-contrast microscope, the antigen-antibody combination shows clearly in dark contrast ; presumably because of the coagulation of the antigen. By this means the capsule of certain *Bacillus* species has been demonstrated to consist of narrow lamina of polysaccharide and polypeptide elements, with larger masses of polysaccharide at the poles of the bacilli, and at the cross-walls. The cell wall can also be made visible when it reacts with the homologous antibody.

Non-specific proteins will also enter into a salt-like combination with capsular components at appropriate values of pH, rendering them visible by phase-contrast microscopy.

These methods can be used with even greater success if the structures are separated by partial digestion with such enzymes as lysozyme or trypsin.

The further development of these techniques, by the use of antibodies specific for cytoplasmic and nuclear components offers a most promising field for study in the cytology of bacteria and other cells also.

These papers should be read in the original for full descriptions of this elaborate technique.

FIG. 6

DEMONSTRATION OF CAPSULES BY TOMCSIK'S METHOD

These photomicrographs were made by Tomcsik's method for specific demonstration of antigenically active material by phase-contrast microscopy. The reaction of the antigen *in situ* with the antibody prepared against a chemically defined extract or suspension renders the structure in question visible to phase-contrast, and gives a simultaneous demonstration of its form and chemical composition. All plates are of a capsulated species of *Bacillus* × 2500.

(1) Capsulated bacteria without added antibody.

(2) The same, with the addition of an antibody active against the polypeptide fraction of the capsule.

(3) The same field as (2) with the further addition of an antibody active against the polysaccharide fraction.

It will be observed that the untreated capsule shows only as a diffuse, pale zone ; after the addition of the polypeptide antibody it appears clearly defined but homogeneous, but the addition of the polysaccharide antibody reveals an unsuspected striated structure, with larger dark areas at the poles and points of division.

(4, 6) Originally non-capsulated bacteria which have developed a secondary capsule in a centrifuged deposit at room temperature. Polysaccharide antibody reveals exceptionally thick capsular septa, occasionally splitting in division.

(5, 7) The same as (4, 6) demonstrated by polypeptide antibody. In this case the polysaccharide septa appear as gaps in the capsule.

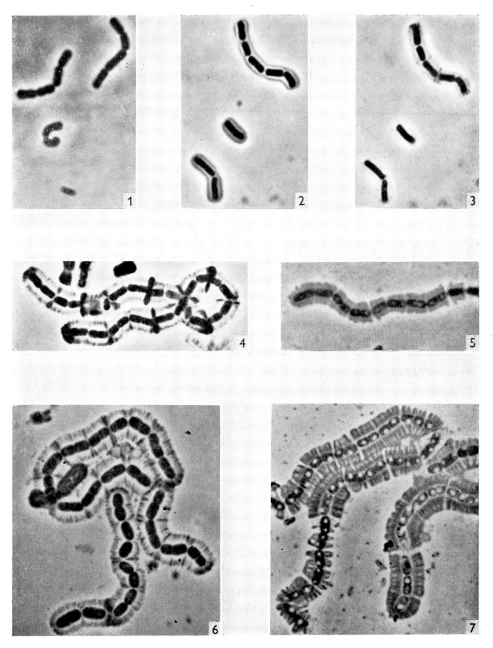

FIG. 6

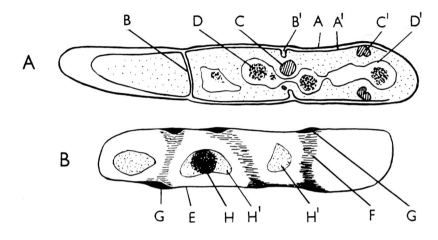

Fig. 7

SECTIONS OF BACTERIA

Diagrams drawn from electron micrographs of *Bacillus cereus* are compared.   Diagram *A* is taken from the study by Chapman and Hillier, and *B* from material prepared in this laboratory.   The former has been treated with 2% osmium tetroxide which has had the effect of rendering the cell wall very clearly visible but may also have coagulated the softer structures. Section *B* has been accorded minimal treatment before embedding.   The cell envelopes are much less clearly seen, but the arrangement of the various structures is in closer accordance with that seen in stained preparations.

A—the cell wall has an outer (*A*) and an inner (*A¹*) layer ; the latter may or may not correspond to the cell membrane.   The cross-walls are seen complete (*B*) and developing by ingrowth (*B¹*) ; an important observation.   The material (*C*) between the inner boundaries of the developing cross-wall, and (*C¹*) at an early stage of their formation, corresponds to the basophilic septum which precedes the true cross-wall.   Its present appearance may well be an artefact arising from the coagulation of a much thinner, continuous structure across the cell.   Similarly, the extension of the matrix (*D¹*), in which the nuclei (*D*) are embedded now extends across the former cell boundaries, at (*B¹*) and (*C¹*).

B—The cell wall (*E*) and cross-walls (*F*) have thickenings (*G*) at their junctions, such as can be observed by phase-contrast by the method of Tomcsik, and in some stained preparations.   The cross-walls are indistinct but continuous ; their mode of development cannot be discerned.   The matrix (*H¹*) of the nuclear bodies (*H*) does not extend across the cell boundaries where these have remained complete.

M: COLONY PREPARATIONS
(5, 6, 7)

Although a bacterial surface colony upon solid medium is a semi-artificial formation, the study of its minute structure is often of biological interest and diagnostic importance. It is capable of providing evidence of the natural relationship of the bacteria to one another, and, especially in the study of dissociation, may indicate differences in structure and behaviour which are not always obvious by other methods of examination.

Entire colonies may be embedded and sectioned, like portions of tissue, but as the colonies are usually exceedingly thin and flat (much more so than they appear to the unaided eye), whole mounts may be made upon slides or coverslips. These are usually termed impression preparations. They are best made from very small colonies, although quite large ones can be mounted if the growth is sufficiently tough.

A small piece of medium bearing the desired colonies, is cut out with the point of a knife and placed, face downward, upon a slide or coverslip. Surface tension will suffice to keep the medium, and the attached colonies, firmly pressed to the glass. It is then fixed, in its entirety, preferably in Bouin's solution, until the medium is blanched throughout, and can be peeled away from the glass, leaving the colonies adhering to the surface of the coverslip. The preparations may then be washed, stained and mounted. Sometimes they are of great beauty.

The best medium for this purpose is blood agar. It is very adhesive when fixed, and becomes firmly attached to the glass, so that it can be peeled away without danger of sliding the medium laterally and destroying the colony. Plates should be inoculated with the rounded tip of a glass rod, to avoid scratching the surface, they should be perfectly dry, and free from bubbles and other irregularities.

N: SUMMARY

The examination of bacteria in dried, heat-fixed smears, stained by the usual diagnostic methods, fails to give a true picture of their morphology.

Bacteria are best examined in water mounted preparations. Their internal structures, especially the nuclear material, are often obscured by the concentration of stainable ribose nucleoprotein in the cytoplasm and cell membrane. This may be removed by hydrolysis or enzyme action, and the nucleus demonstrated by a variety of staining methods. The nuclear material may also be stained, with more difficulty, by classical cytological techniques. It reacts chemically as though composed mainly of deoxyribose nucleoprotein.

The cell membrane stains with lipid-soluble dyes, and transverse septa derived from it also stain very strongly with basic dyes.

The cell wall resists staining unless mordanted with tannic or phosphomolybdic acid which also destroys the protein structures of the cell.

The staining of flagella and capsular material and the technique of colony impressions are described.

Considerable advances have been made in the application of electron and phase-contrast microscopy, as applied to bacterial cytology. In particular, the preparation of electron-transparent sections, and the use of enzymes, antibodies and proteins in a manner analogous to specific staining, for phase-contrast microscopy, have shown promise of providing valuable information.

BIBLIOGRAPHY

(1) ALLEN, L. A., APPLEBY, J. C. and WOLF, J. (1939) Zbl. f. Bakt. II. 100. 3.
(2) BADIAN, J. (1933) Arch. f. Mikrobiol. 4. 409.
(3) BEEBE, J. M. (1941) J. Bact. 42. 193.
(4) BIRCH-ANDERSEN, A., MAALØE, O. and SÖJSTRAND, F. S. (1953) Biochim. Biophys Acta. 12. 395.
(5) BISSET, K. A. (1938) J. Path. Bact. 47. 223.
(6) BISSET, K. A. (1939a) ibid. 48. 427.
(7) BISSET, K. A. (1939b) ibid. 49. 491.
(8) BISSET, K. A. (1947) J. Gen. Microbiol. 2. 83.
(9) BISSET, K. A. (1948a) ibid. 2. 126.
(10) BISSET, K. A. (1948b) J. Hyg., Camb. 46. 264.
(11) BISSET, K. A. (1949) J. Gen. Microbiol. 3. 93.
(12) BISSET, K. A. (1953) Stain Technol. 28. 45.
(13) BISSET, K. A. (1954a) J. Bact. 67. 41.

(14) Bisset, K. A. (1954b) Exp. Cell. Res. 7. 232.

(15) Bisset, K. A. and Hale, C. M. F. (1951) J. Hyg., Camb. 49. 201.

(16) Bisset, K. A. and Hale, C. M. F. (1953) J. Gen. Microbiol. 8. 442.

(17) Brachet, J. (1940) C. R. Soc. Biol. 133. 88.

(18) Burdon, K. L. (1946) J. Bact. 52. 665.

(19) Cassel, W. A. (1950) J. Bact. 59. 185.

(20) Chance, H. L. (1953) Stain Technol. 28. 205.

(21) Chapman, G. B. and Hillier, J. (1953) J. Bact. 66. 362.

(22) Clark, J. B., Galyen, L. I. and Webb, R. B. (1953) Stain Technol. 28. 313.

(23) Clifton, C. E. and Ehrhard, H. (1952) J. Bact. 63. 537.

(24) Delamater, E. D. (1951) Stain Technol. 26. 199.

(25) Dubos, R. J. (1937) Science. 85. 549.

(26) Dyer, M. T. (1947) J. Bact. 53. 498.

(27) Eisenberg, P. (1910) Zbl. f. Bakt. I. 53. 481.

(28) Hale, C. M. F. (1953) Lab. Practice. 2. 115.

(29) Hale, C. M. F. (1954) Exp. Cell. Res. 6. 243.

(30) Hillier, J., Mudd, S. and Smith, A. G. (1949) J. Bact. 57. 319.

(31) Henry, H. and Stacey, M. (1943) Nature, Lond. 151. 671.

(32) Henry, H. and Stacey, M. (1946) Proc. Roy. Soc. B. 133. 391.

(33) Houwink, A. L. (1953) Biochim. Biophys. Acta. 10. 360.

(34) Hurst, H. (1952) J. Exp. Biol. 29. 30.

(35) Iterson, W. van (1947) Biochim. Biophys. Acta. 1. 527.

(36) Klieneberger-Nobel, E. (1947) J. Gen. Microbiol. 1. 33.

(37) Klieneberger-Nobel, E. (1948) J. Hyg., Camb. 46. 345.

(38) Knaysi, G. (1946) J. Bact. 51. 113.

(39) Mitchell, P. (1949) Symposium : " The Nature of the Bacterial Surface," Oxford,
Blackwell.

(40) Mitchell, P. and Moyle, J. (1950) Nature, Lond. 166. 218.

(41) Mitchell, P. and Moyle, J. (1954) J. Gen. Microbiol. 10. 533.

(42) Moller, V. and Birch-Andersen, A. (1951) Act. Path. Microbiol. Scand. 29. 132.

(43) Mudd, S. et al. (1951) J. Bact. 62. 729.

(44) Murray, R. G. E. (1953) Symp. Bact. Cytol., Rome. VI. Int. Cong. Microbiol.

(45) Murray, R. G. E. and Robinow, C. F. (1952) J. Bact. 63. 298.

(46) Pennington, D. (1950) J. Bact. 59. 617.

(47) Paillot, A. (1919) Ann. Inst. Past. 33. 403.

(48) Piekarski, G. (1937) Arch. f. Mikrobiol. 8. 428.

(49) Piekarski, G. (1938) Zbl. f. Bakt. I. 142. 69.

(50) Piekarski, G. (1939) ibid. 144. 140.

(51) Robinow, C. F. (1942) Proc. Roy. Soc. B. 130. 299.

(52) Robinow, C. F. (1944) J. Hyg. Camb. 43. 413.

(53) Robinow, C. F. (1945) Addendum to : " The Bacterial Cell." Dubos, R. J. Harvard
Univ. Press.

(54) Robinow, C. F. and Cosslett, V. E. (1948) J. Appl. Phys. 19. 124.

(55) Robinow, C. F. (1953) J. Bact. 66. 300.

(56) ROBINOW, C. F. and MURRAY, R. G. E. (1953) Exp. Cell. Res. 40. 390.

(57) STILLE, B. (1937) Arch. f. Mikrobiol. 8. 125.

(58) STOUGHTON, R. H. (1929) Proc. Roy. Soc. B. 105. 469.

(59) STOUGHTON, R. H. (1932) ibid. 111. 46.

(60) TOMCSIK, J. and GUEX-HOLZER, S. (1951) Schweiz. Zeit. f. Allg. Path. u. Bakt. 14. 515.

(61) TOMCSIK, J. and GUEX-HOLZER, S. (1952) ibid. 15. 517.

(62) TOMCSIK, J. and GUEX-HOLZER, S. (1953) ibid. 16. 882.

(63) TOMCSIK, J. and GUEX-HOLZER, S. (1954a) J. Gen. Microbiol. 10. 97.

(64) TOMCSIK, J. and GUEX-HOLZER, S. (1954b) ibid. 10. 317.

(65) TULASNE, R. and VENDRELY, R. (1948) Nature, Lond. 161. 316.

(66) WEBB, R. B. (1954) J. Bact. 67. 252.

(67) WEIBULL, C. (1953a) ibid. 66. 137.

(68) WEIBULL, C. (1953b) ibid. 66. 688.

CHAPTER III

Surface Structures

A: THE CELL WALL

(1, 2, 5-12, 15-20, 24, 25, 26, 28, 29, 30, 32, 33, 35, 36, 40, 43-46, 49, 50, 52, 55, 56, 59, 61, 68, 69, 70, 71, 72, 74, 75, 77, 78, 81, 83-88, 93, 94, 95, 97, 98, 103, 104, 105)

BACTERIA are of such small size that the adoption, in a fluid medium, of any other form than that of a sphere, argues considerable rigidity of structure. Were this rigidity absent, the forces of surface tension, relatively enormous in such a case, would force the bacterium to adopt the form possessing the smallest proportion of surface area to volume. While it is true that some bacteria are almost perfect spheres, although these are rather fewer than is often supposed, the majority are rod-shaped, usually slightly spiral, and sometimes more markedly spiral so that this feature is sufficiently obvious to attract attention. Their rigidity is further emphasised by the absence of flexion in their movements, except in certain specialised forms such as myxobacteria. An appearance of flexion is often given by the rapid rotation of spiral cells, but this is almost certainly an optical illusion. Enforced flexion causes fracture and distortion of the bacterium. This rigidity is due to the possession of a cell wall of great strength.

An understanding of the nature and behaviour of the cell wall and membranes of bacteria is a necessary preliminary to studies of all kinds in bacterial cytology. Neglect to acquire such an understanding has had the regrettable effect of invalidating a great deal of otherwise sound and con-scientious work, as well as of emphasising the defects of some to which no such description can be applied.

The most usual and indeed the most fundamental error which arises from such neglect is the assumption, so frequently made, that bacteria are normally unicellular, whereas in very many groups, ranging in morphology from

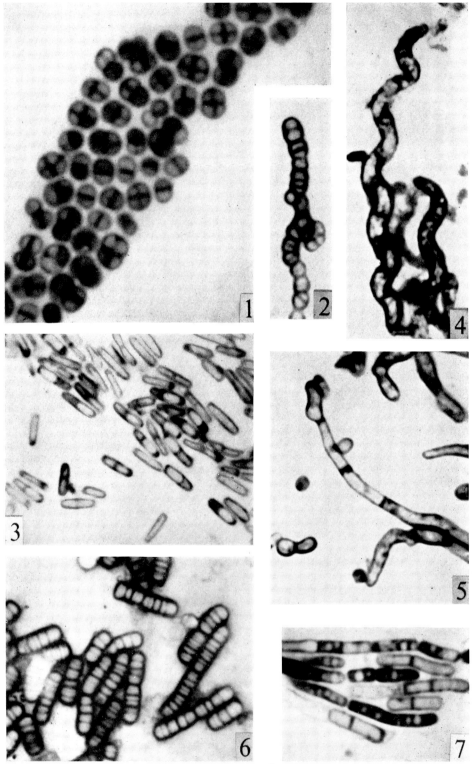

((5, 6, 7) *reproduced from Experimental Cell Research*)

FIG. 8

cocci to branched filaments, a single bacterium may contain from two to a dozen relatively tiny cells. The partitions between these cells may break down in the course of the autogamous processes which accompany sporulation, and at other times, but are usually found in the vegetative cells.

The cell wall is permeable, it does not grow, but is secreted, in certain well-marked areas, by the semi-permeable cell membrane which underlies it. Measurements of electron micrographs of sectioned bacteria suggest that its thickness varies from 100 to 250 Ångstrom units.

The cell wall is difficult to demonstrate and is seldom observed in preparations stained by the usual methods of routine bacteriology. Under such conditions, the existence of the cross-walls is liable to pass unsuspected. The cross-walls are laid down, in the dividing cell, by cytoplasmic septa which stain well with basic dyes, and when the multicellular structure of such bacteria goes unrecognised these basophilic septa are liable to be confused with nuclear structures and other cytoplasmic inclusions.

The complex cellular structure of many bacteria has long been known but seldom adequately appreciated until Robinow (1945, *q.v.* also for earlier literature) demonstrated beyond any reasonable doubt the structure and type of cell division in both unicellular and multicellular bacteria. The former divide by constriction of the cell wall, the latter by the formation of complete cross-walls, which subsequently split.

FIG. 8

CELL DIVISION IN BACTERIA

Cell division, in various bacterial types ; stained by Hale's method. All at × 3000 except (1), × 4,500, and (6) × 1,700.

(1) Typical multicellular coccus. Each unit, which appears by routine staining methods as a single, spherical cell, contains two, four or more cells, separated by cross-walls, each of which is formed at right-angles to the preceding.

(2) *Streptococcus* sp. Although each coccus may contain two or more cells, the cross-walls are all in the same plane.

(3) Typical unicellular bacterium (*Pseudomonas* sp.). Dividing cells are separated by a short-lived septum, lacking the rigidity of a true cross-wall. Frequently one pole, the growing point, is marked by a concentration of stainable material.

(4) *Spirillum* sp. (modified stain by Mr R. A. Fox). The cross-walls of spirilla are not easy to demonstrate, nor, in view of their differences of plane, to photograph, but they appear to be true cross-walls, comparable with those of the Gram-positive genera.

(5) *Nocardia rhodnii*. Irregular septation with transient branching of the filaments.

(6) *Caryophanon latum*. The highest degree of multicellularity is seen in these giant, intestinal bacteria, where each cell is reduced to a disc.

(7) An exceptional degree of irregular multicellularity is seen in aberrant stains of *Bacillus cereus*, and this appearance is accentuated by their high lipid content.

These two methods of cell-division are correlated with the " smooth " and the " rough " filamentous morphological types of bacteria respectively. Parallel types occur in coccal genera, most of which contain two, four or more cells in each coccus. Four cells is normal number in many cocci, commonly regarded as unicellular.

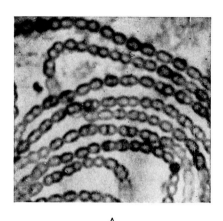
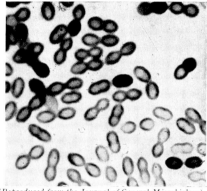

(*Reproduced from the Journal of General Microbiology*).

A   B

Fig. 9

BEHAVIOUR OF THE CELL WALL IN DIVIDING STREPTOCOCCI

A. Long-chained streptoccus. Division is by the production of cross-walls, each parallel to the last, exactly as in rough bacilli.

B. Short-chained streptococcus. Division is by constriction of the cell wall.

All stained by tannic-acid-violet × 3000.

A multicellular structure, sometimes with as many as twenty cells, separated by cross-walls and cytoplasmic septa, in each bacterium, has been demonstrated in nearly all Gram-positive bacteria. An extreme multicellularity is found in the giant bacteria such as *Caryophanon* and *Oscillospira*.

That the multicellularity of these bacteria is fundamental, and by no means a superficial subdivision of filaments by the irregular growth of septa, is shown by the observation of Tomcsik (1951), that in *Bacillus anthracis* the characteristic division of the bacillus into four small cells extends also to the polypeptide capsule, in which lines of demarcation can be seen, corresponding to the positions of the cross-walls internally.

Until recently, very little was known of the composition of bacterial cell walls, although the evidence suggested that they resembled the cell walls of plants in containing a large polysaccharide fraction, together with lipid and nitrogenous components. Some parts of the lipid component probably belongs to the cell membrane. Holdsworth (1952a, 1952b) isolated a protein-carbohydrate complex from the cell wall of *Corynebacterium diphtheriae*, in

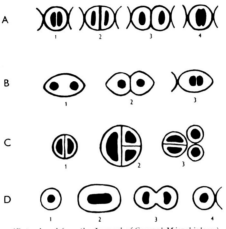

(Reproduced from the Journal of General Microbiology.)

FIG. 10

CELL DIVISION IN COCCI

    A. Long-chained streptococcus, corresponding approximately to a rough bacillus. Division is by the production of transverse septa.

    B. Short-chained streptococcus, corresponding to a smooth bacillus. Division is by constriction of the cell wall, and each nuclear unit represents a chromosome pair (Chapter IV).

    C. Septate staphylococcus. Resembles *A*, except that each septum is produced at right-angles to the preceding one. This morphology is also typical of the Gram-negative " diplococci."

    D. Unicellular coccus. Division is by constriction, but the organism possesses a central, spherical nucleus (Chapter IV).

which the protein component differed in constitution from the intracellular proteins. Holdsworth claims that the carbohydrate fraction is an oligo-saccharide and polysaccharides have also been described from the same source. Histochemically the cell walls and cross-walls of *C. diphtheriae* and many other species of bacteria can be demonstrated to contain polysaccharides, by the use of periodic acid.

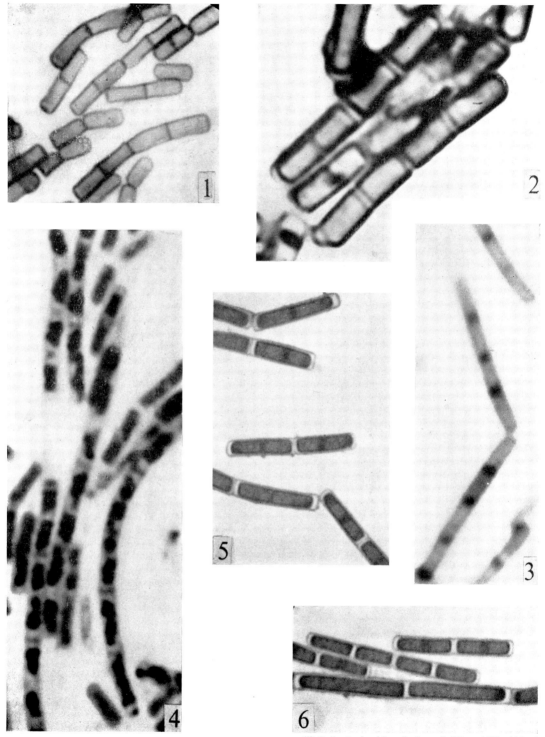

((2, 3, 4) *reproduced from the Journal of General Microbiology*).

Fɪɢ. 11

Perhaps surprisingly, the lipid element is an important factor in the maintenance of the considerable structural rigidity of the cell wall. If it is removed the strength of the structure is greatly reduced.

Differences exist between the nature and composition of the cell walls of Gram-positive and Gram-negative bacteria. Those from Gram-negative genera have a higher lipid content and a much fuller range of amino-acids in the protein fraction; and their cytochemical behaviour more closely resembles that of intact wool proteins, whereas Gram-positive bacteria resemble degraded wool proteins in this respect. These observations may serve partially to explain the greater apparent rigidity of the cell walls of Gram-negative bacteria, which can form relatively long filaments without the necessity of the cross-walls which Gram-positive genera produce under the same circumstances. They are also very interesting from the immuno-logical viewpoint; the great complexity of the cell wall proteins of Gram-negative bacteria is almost certainly correlated with their more satisfactory behaviour as antigens, whereas in the rough variants of *Bacteriaceae* the loss of antigenic specificity is associated with a change to the septate morphology and mode of cell division characteristic of Gram-positive bacilli. In addition,

Fig. 11

CELL ENVELOPES IN *BACILLUS*

In "rough" septate bacilli the bacillus is usually divided centrally by a complete cross cell wall and subdivided by developing cross-walls at varying stages. The latter may stain as cell walls or cell membranes (*i.e.* basophilic) according to the stage of development.

(1) *B. cereus*, cell walls by Hale's method. Demonstrating only mature cross-walls × 3000.

(2) *B. megaterium*, cell walls by tannic-acid-violet. Cross-walls at various stages can be seen; the most mature appear double, possibly because of tannic-acid complex deposited on their faces. × 4,500.

(3) *B. megaterium* stained by haematoxylin. Developing cross-walls show as dark bars; the cell wall does not stain. Such basophilic areas have frequently been mistaken for nuclei or portions of nuclear structures. × 4,500.

(4) *B. megaterium* stained by acid-thionin. This dye is less specific for the nuclear structures than Giemsa and stains also the basophilic areas of developing cross-walls, which appear either as readily recognisable bars or else as dots between the nuclei. In the latter form they have been confused with mitotic centrioles. × 4,500.

(5), (6) Cell walls and cell membranes stained simultaneously by the Victoria blue method of Robinow and Murray (1953). The bacilli (*B. megaterium*) are slightly plasmolysed and the cell membrane is retracted from the mature cross-walls. The developing cross-walls show as dark bars, apparently composed of, or surrounded by, the same material as the cell membrane. × 3,000.

Gram-negative cell walls alone show birefringence, and they cannot so readily be freed from the cell membrane by plasmolysis.

Cytological studies of the cell wall, especially those by Robinow, Klieneberger-Nobel, Bisset and Morris, have owed much to the technique of Eisenberg (1910), perfected by Robinow (1945) of mordanting with tannic acid, which renders it possible to stain the otherwise resistant cell wall with basic dyes, and at the same time destroys the stainability of the cell proteins which enclose and mask the cross-walls and other internal structures. Probably, in addition, the cytoplasmic proteins are precipitated to some extent on the interior of the cell wall, which assists in rendering the outline of the walls stainable by basic dyes. An even better staining method (Hale, 1953), employing phosphomolybdic acid as a mordant, probably acts in the same way, since these agents are alike in being protein precipitants. The fact that the mature cross-walls resist their action, whereas the basophilic septa are destroyed, constitutes some degree of confirmation for the hypothesis that the latter consist of protein whereas the former contain a large polysaccharide component.

The cross-walls can be seen very easily in bacteria which have been crushed or disrupted and partially emptied of their cell contents. By electron microscopy it is only in such material, or in sections, that the septate structure of bacteria can be discerned. However, the desiccation of material prepared for this method of examination may cause the cellular structure of such markedly septate organisms as *Mycobacterium* to manifest itself in the form of a row of granules, rather like their beaded appearance in Ziehl-Neelsen stained preparations. In electron microscope studies by workers apparently unaware of the septate structure of *Mycobacterium*, these granules have been identified with a variety of intracellular structures, for example, nuclei, sap-vacuoles, and mitochondria.

It is not suggested that none of the structures described form part of these granular aggregates, indeed the nuclei must necessarily do so ; but the identification of a structure which comprises so high a proportion of any one of the relatively tiny component cells of these multicellular bacteria with any single cytoplasmic component, on the evidence of a fancied resemblance in an electron micrograph, is exceedingly difficult to justify.

By comparison of electron micrographs of crushed or sectioned bacteria of septate and non-septate morphology an independent verification of these observations, made upon stained material, by classical microscopy, has now been established.

B: THE CELL MEMBRANE

(2, 3, 4, 8, 9, 11, 15, 17, 18, 20, 21, 22, 26, 27, 31, 39, 41, 42, 43, 46, 57, 58, 65, 66, 67, 71, 72, 77, 81, 83, 86, 87, 88, 91, 98, 102, 103, 104)

Little is known of the structure of the cell membrane. Extensive studies have been made upon its physico-chemical behaviour, but these are beyond the scope of the present work. A few observations have been made upon its chemical constitution, but fewer than in the case of the cell wall. It appears to be a semi-permeable membrane about 100 Ångstrom units in thickness.

Unlike the cell wall, the underlying cytoplasmic membrane, which constitutes the osmotic barrier of the cell, is embarrassingly easily stained by almost any method. This applies especially to the cytoplasmic septa and the growing points, which are associated with the membrane. These structures are highly basophilic, so much so that they will stain well with many dyes supposedly specific for chromatin, mitochondria, reticulocytes, etc. The entire cell membrane has a high content of nucleoproteins, but these are especially concentrated in the growing points, and it is interesting to consider the observation of Pijper (1938) that somatic agglutination occurs by the adherence of the bacteria at the tips of the cells. Not only is the cell wall very thin at this point, being in the process of formation, but one of the main aggregations of nucleoproteins in the cell membrane occurs immediately underneath, so that it would appear that the growing points, and presumably also the almost identical cytoplasmic septa, may be a major somatic antigen.

The nucleic acids in the cell membrane are almost unquestionably res-ponsible for the ease with which the entire bacteria can be stained, and when this stainable cortex is viewed through the tips of the cell, the well-known optical illusion of " bipolar staining " is observable, sometimes reinforced by the appearance of the basophilic growing points. The nucleic acids are also claimed to cause the phenomenon of Gram-positivity, where it occurs (Henry

C

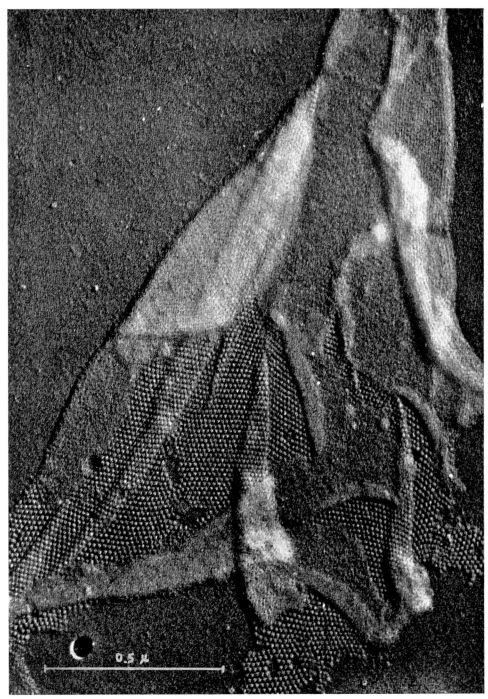

Fig. 12

and Stacey, 1943 ; Henry, Stacey and Teece, 1945).   According to these
authorities it is the difference in proportion of ribose and deoxyribose nucleic
acids which determines the Gram-reaction, the former being preponderant
in Gram-positive bacteria.   On the other hand Mitchell and Moyle (1950)
attribute Gram-positivity to the presence of a phosphoric ester, the occurrence
of which is independent of the concentration of ribose nucleic acid.   Hoffman
(1951) suggests that a difference in the tyrosine content of the pentose nucleoproteins of Gram-positive and Gram-negative bacteria might account for
the difference.

As in other types of cell, the cell membrane contains an element which
stains with lipid-soluble dyes, and there is little reason to doubt that it is
similar in most respects to the cell membranes which are, perhaps, the most
important organs of any living cell, and which serve to insulate the cell
contents from the effects of variation in the outside medium by the exercise
of a regulatory function upon the passage of dissolved material through their
surface.

The actual demonstration of the cell-membrane as a separate structure has
been achieved in lysozyme digested bacteria by Weibull (1953 *b, c*) and Tomcsik
and Guex-Holzer (1954).   In the last stages of dissolution, the protoplasts appeared
as " ghosts," and the empty membrane survived momentarily.   The behaviour
of the cell membrane at cell division provides additional evidence that it is a
positive structure, and not merely an altered surface or interface.   The septa
which initiate cell division are clearly resoluble, although surrounded on both
sides by cytoplasm.

The large quantity of nucleic acids contained in, or associated with the
cell membrane may be a cause of confusion.   It is observed that, as in the case
of plant cells, the effect of certain cytological procedures, for example formalin
fixation or acid-hydrolysis, may be to increase the basophilia of the nucleus

---

FIG. 12

ELECTRON MICROSCOPY OF CELL ENVELOPE MATERIAL

Spirillum sp., wall of crushed cell.   The outer layer is represented by the striated pattern
in the upper part of the plate, the inner by the pattern of regular globules below.   Although
not conclusive in itself, this appearance is in accordance with the view that the envelope
comprises an outer polysaccharide and an inner protein layer.   (× 100,000).

at the expense of that of the cell envelopes. Experimentally, it can be shown that DNA of extrinsic origin may become adsorbed upon the bacterial cell envelopes in the form of granules of very deceptive appearance. The possibility of a transfer of nucleic acids between the nucleus and cell envelopes must always be taken into consideration whenever small, basophilic structures are under examination.

Septa of a different and specialised type, with an active basophilic component are found in the mother-cells of *Rhizobium* swarmers. These fundamentally resemble the polysaccharide-complex cross-walls of *Bacillus* species and are lined on both sides with basophilic material resembling the normal, membranous septa, but greatly thickened. They appear to provide a secretory lining to the lumen of the cells wherein the tiny swarmers are formed. The misconceptions which have arisen from the appearance of these " barred cells " are discussed in a later section : (Chapter VII).

A recent and very important study on the differentiation of the cell wall, membrane and cytoplasm by Robinow and Murray (1953), should be read in the original by all who are interested in this subject.

C: DEVELOPMENT OF THE CELL ENVELOPES

(3, 6, 7, 8, 9, 15, 18, 19, 29, 30, 64, 71, 72, 81, 86, 87, 92, 93, 94, 95, 96, 97, 98)

The fundamentals of bacterial cell division described by Schaudinn (1902) 1903) have been well substantiated by later work. The two main morphological types of bacteria, which correspond to the " smooth " and " rough " colony forms, divide by constriction of the cell wall and by the formation of cross-walls respectively. In the " rough " type, which is especially typical of the large, Gram-positive bacilli, the division of the cells by cross-walls proceeds more rapidly than does their complete separation, so that the coiled bands of filaments are formed which give the well-known " Medusa-head " colony appearance. The actual separation of rough bacilli does not necessarily occur immediately after the completion of cell division. Nor, when it does occur, is it invariably the most longstanding cross wall which is split, although this is usually the case. Separation may occur in such a manner as regularly to produce one large and one small daughter bacillus, *i.e.* containing more and less cells.

Filaments of a different type, without cross-walls, are formed in a more elaborate, probably syngamous type of cell division, which occurs in many different bacterial groups. These filaments eventually fragment to form new bacterial units.

In all forms of cell division, the new cell wall material, whether it appears as a constriction or as a complete cross wall, is secreted by a basophilic septum derived from the cell membrane, which appears across the cell as the first sign of incipient division, exactly as in certain types of plant cell. The constrictive ingrowths are secreted at the points of junction of the cell wall and cross-walls or septum, and in the septate bacilli and cocci it is here that the main growth of the cell wall proceeds. The new surface is, as it were, passed outwards around the edge of the internal division between the cells to the outside surface. The work of Tomcsik (1954) confirms that the main growth of the capsule is also at this point, where a distinct thickening of the cell wall can be observed by his methods. A similar thickening can be observed also in sections of bacteria prepared in this laboratory. In the unicellular, non-septate types the new cell wall is formed at the point of division and also at the tips of the cell ; usually only at one tip, the growing point. The point of division becomes the growing point of one or both of the daughter cells, so that there is no fundamental difference between the septa and the growing points.

In very young cultures division may be so rapid that a single bacillus is subdivided into three or four cells, by septa derived from the cell membrane, while the process of ingrowth of the wall is incomplete.

The evidence of the growth of " smooth " bacteria, and the formation of the cell wall at a growing point at one tip is derived from several sources. The first is the arrangement of the surface structures and especially the flagella in electron micrographs of growing and dividing bacteria and germinating microcysts. In such cells the flagella appear progressively shorter towards one pole where the wall is relatively thin, flexible and electron-transparent. Frequently one daughter cell may be provided with a full quota of well-developed flagella, whereas the other has very short flagella or none. It appears that newly formed cell envelopes develop their flagella by outgrowth over an appreciable period of time, and the progressive immaturity of the flagella towards the pole which exhibits a thin area of cell wall indicates that the wall itself is more recently formed at that end of the cell, and that in effect it grows from that pole. It is, in any case, logical to assume that a rigid yet " dead " structure, such as a cell wall, would form in this manner. It could not grow all over its surface, but could approximate to doing so only by constantly tearing and reforming, of which there is no evidence. In those multicellular bacteria which, as described above, form the cell wall at a number of growing points at the junctions of the cell walls and cross-walls (*i.e.* at the poles of the individual cells), an appearance of uniform growth is given.

Further information upon the subject of growing points is derived from the researches of Bergersen (1952) upon the effect of sub-lethal concentrations of chloramphenicol on *Bact. coli*. The bacteria developed typical basophilic concentrations in the cell membrane at various points, and from these grew irregular side-branches. As these branches enlarged the growing points remained at the tip so long as growth persisted, retaining their basophilic character indicative of the presence of metabolically active nucleoproteins. The growing points, like all such metabolically-active areas, are also centres of oxidation-reduction activity, and for this reason have been equated with mitochondria by some authorities. However, they bear no resemblance to

Fig. 13

CELL ENVELOPES

The cell envelopes observable by electron microscopy. Owing to the opacity of the bacterial cell, little can be seen in most intact specimens under the electron microscope ; however, in sectioned or accidentally disrupted material some detail can be observed.

(1) *Bacillus cereus*, section showing one complete cross-wall and a second at an early stage of ingrowth. The inner edge of the incomplete septum is lined with material which probably represents the cytoplasmic septum preceding and secreting the new cell wall material, but which may be coagulated by the osmium tetroxide with which the preparation has been treated.   × 50,000.

(2) Cell wall of partially disrupted *Spirillum* sp., showing striated structure and blepharoplasts at the bases of the compound flagella.   × 20,000.

(3) Cell envelopes of partially disrupted *Pseudomonas* sp. ; the cell wall is transparent and apparently simple ; the blepharoplasts are visible at the bases of the flagella ; the emergent protoplast still appears to be covered by a membrane.   × 10,000.

(4) Where the structure is sufficiently small to be electron transparent the cross-walls can be demonstrated in the intact organism, as in the stalks of *Caulobacter*, which are extensions of the body wall.   × 15,000.

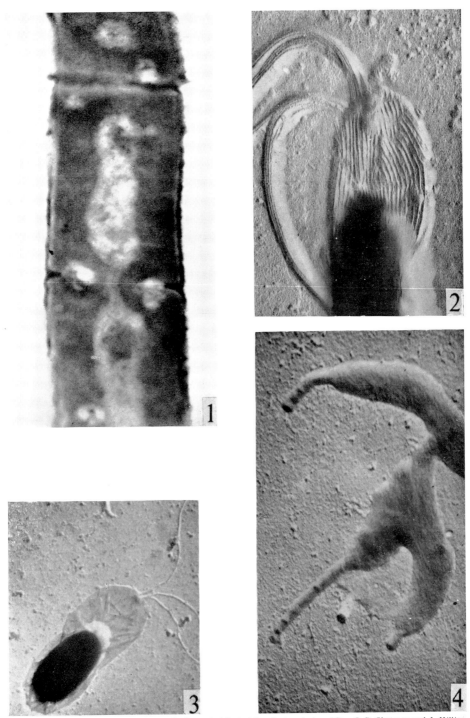

((1) *Reproduced from the Journal of Bacteriology by permission of Drs. G. B. Chapman and J. Hillier*)
((2) *Reproduced by permission of Miss P. E Pease*)

FIG. 13

mitochondria in form, arrangement, or, so far as is known, in function, and this interpretation has been severely criticised.

D: THE CELL WALL OF MYXOBACTERIA
(54, 62, 89, 90)

The myxobacteria differ from most other bacteria in that they lack the rigid cell wall, and are independent of flagella for motility.

No cell wall whatever can be detected in myxobacteria by ordinary staining methods, but its existence, and some of its structural characteristics, can be inferred from other considerations. Although the cells exhibit some degree of flexibility, their structure is sufficiently rigid to enable them to retain the bacillary form when immersed in fluid. Such strength would unquestionably not be possessed by the unprotected cell membrane.

Myxobacteria are motile only when in contact with a surface, whether a solid surface or the surface film of a fluid. They show a marked inclination to move along the lines of physical stress in the surface, a phenomenon which has been described as elasticotaxis. Their mode of progression has been variously described, but appears to the author to be a worm-like action analogous to peristalsis. Flexion is occasionally shown but probably is not a necessary function of locomotion.

This implies a muscular activity in the cell wall, which must be capable of contracting circumferentially, to extend the cell, and also longitudinally, to shorten and expand the cell. Muscular action in so small an organ is not exceptional and is obvious in the locomotory cilia and flagella of many small creatures, including bacteria. It may therefore be presumed that the cell wall of myxobacteria comprises a longitudinal and circular system of contractile fibres, which enable it to perform the flexion and the peristaltic action which can be observed. It may be regarded as reasonably certain that such contractile fibres are composed of protein, which serves to explain the difference between the chemical reactions of the myxobacterial cell wall and of the polysaccharide structure which is common to most other bacteria.

The microcysts of myxobacteria possess a rigid cell wall which more closely resembles that of eubacteria.

E: THE SPORE COAT
(23, 60, 81, 82)

The resistance of the bacterial spore to inimical agencies has been attributed by some authorities to the impermeable spore coat, and by others to the peculiar condition of the cytoplasm of the spore.

While the spore coat is difficult to stain, it is no more so than the cell wall of vegetative bacteria, from which it does not appear to differ markedly in any respect. Like the cell wall, the spore coat may be partially destroyed by hydrolysis with hydrochloric acid, and it is probably composed mainly of polysaccharide material.

Electron micrographs of sections of spores have shown that the spore coat is a single structure in *Bacillus cereus*, whereas in *B. megaterium* at least two layers can be discerned (Robinow, 1953).

The ejection of the turgid nuclear material from hydrolysed spores indicates that the spore coat possesses a small area of weakness, possibly a germination pore.

F: THE NUCLEAR MEMBRANE
(5, 13, 14, 30)

The apparent absence of a nuclear membrane in bacteria has many times been remarked upon in cytological literature. This is probably due to the fact that bacteria have been examined mainly in their period of active, vegetative growth, when the nucleus is permanently in the chromosomal condition. The resting nucleus has a membrane of normal appearance.

Electron micrographs of sections of bacterial nuclei have shown signs of a fibrous layer surrounding the denser portion of the nucleus.

G: SLIME LAYERS AND CAPSULES
(34, 56, 88, 92, 93, 94, 95, 96, 97, 98)

Many bacteria possess a surface layer of mucoid material, and occasionally a well-defined capsule. The two structures have often been confused, but are distinct and may be found simultaneously.

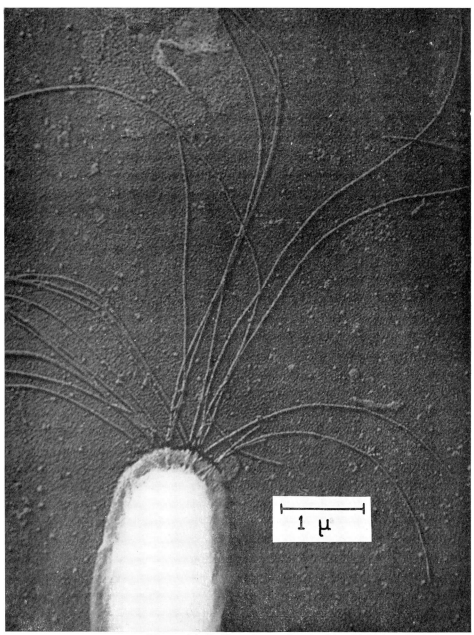

FIG. 14

BACTERIAL FLAGELLA

Spirillum serpens   Gold-shadowed electron micrograph, showing flagella passing through the cell wall to the protoplast.

The phase-contrast studies of Tomcsik, and Tomcsik and Guex-Holzer have revolutionised the previous concept of bacterial capsules as an amorphous layer of polysaccharide or polypeptide mucus, by demonstrating that they may possess an exceedingly complex structure of alternate striations of polysaccharide and polypeptide, perpendicular to the cell wall ; that is parallel to the cross-walls, which are marked by exceptionally massive lamina, as are the poles of the bacilli. The growth of the capsule, like that of the cell wall, occurs mainly at the junctions of the cell wall and cross-walls.

H: FLAGELLA

(15, 16, 21, 22, 38, 47, 48, 50, 51, 53, 63, 77, 78, 79, 99, 100, 101, 103, 104)

Motility in the great majority of bacterial groups is by means of flagella. These number from one to several hundred. They may be arranged singly or in small groups at the poles of the cell, in which case they render their possessor very actively motile in a fluid medium, or they may be arranged in larger numbers peritrichously, which is probably an adaptation to movement in viscous media or on moist surfaces (Chapter IX).

The polar flagella are approximately 26 mμ in diameter, in *Vibrio* and *Pseudomonas* ; the peritrichous flagella may be as small as 19 mμ in *Proteus*. Because of their small size their mode of action is difficult to determine. They have been described as lashing, but more probably act by waves of contraction passing down their fine coils. The wavelength of these coils varies from 2 to 3 μ and is constant for any bacterial species, but variants in a single strain may have flagella of double the normal wavelength.

Flagella point away from the direction of motion, and the rearmost may become twisted together into a spiral thread. Cast-off flagella, in fixed preparations, also tend to knit up into whips in this manner.

The flagella originate in the cell membrane or surface cytoplasm and pass outwards through the cell wall. When the cell wall is removed by digestion with lysozyme, the flagella remain attached to the protoplast. Their point of origin is a basal granule or blepharoplast, approximately spherical and rather larger in diameter than the flagellum which arises from it. In most bacterial genera each flagellum arises from a separate granule, but the flagellar fibrils of spirilla, each of which is about half the diameter of a typical, unfibrillar flagellum, arise in bundles from single granules, so that each bundle constitutes a compound flagellum. This is considered to represent a primitive condition, intermediate between that in typical bacteria and in the flagellate protista (Chapter IX).

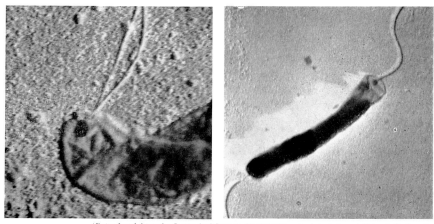

(Reproduced from the Journal of General Microbiology, by permission of Miss J. B. Grace).

A   B

FIG. 15

BACTERIAL BLEPHAROPLASTS

A.   Electron micrograph of *Spirillum* sp. showing two flagella attached to a blepharoplast.
B.   *Vibrio cholerae* with monfibrillar flagellum and its blepharoplast. (*See also figs.* 13, 16, 57).

The microcysts and spores of bacteria are devoid of flagella. These commence to grow at germination ; usually at the pole remote from the growing-point of the cell.

Because of their muscular activity, and because they are complete antigens, flagella are almost certainly composed of protein in all cases. In *Proteus* they have been shown to consist of a fibrous protein resembling myosin. By comparison with the contractile muscle protein actomyosin, however, it lacks the sulphydryl groups which play an important part in this complex.

The possession of flagella is the most important single factor suggesting relationship between bacteria and the flagellate protista, rather than with the blue-green algae, as is often suggested, and much of the argument concerning evolutionary relationships between bacteria is based upon the evidence of these structures.

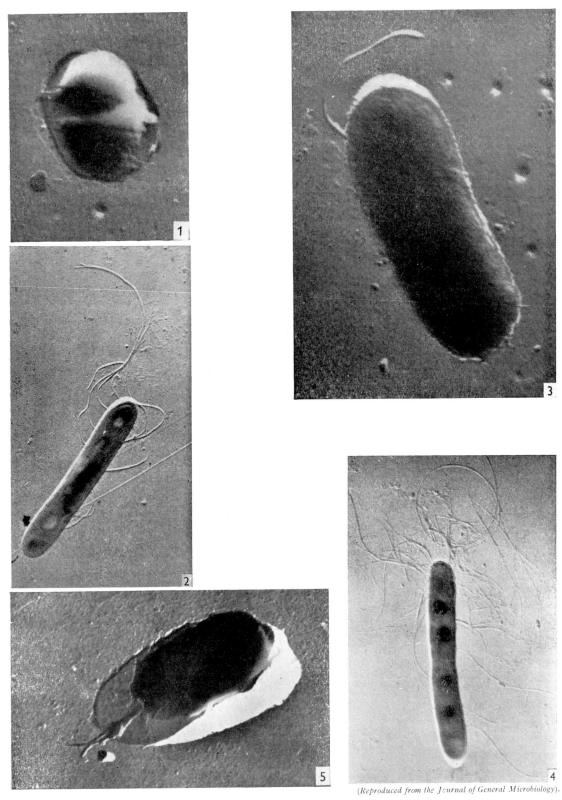

FIG 16
(*See Legend on page* 47)

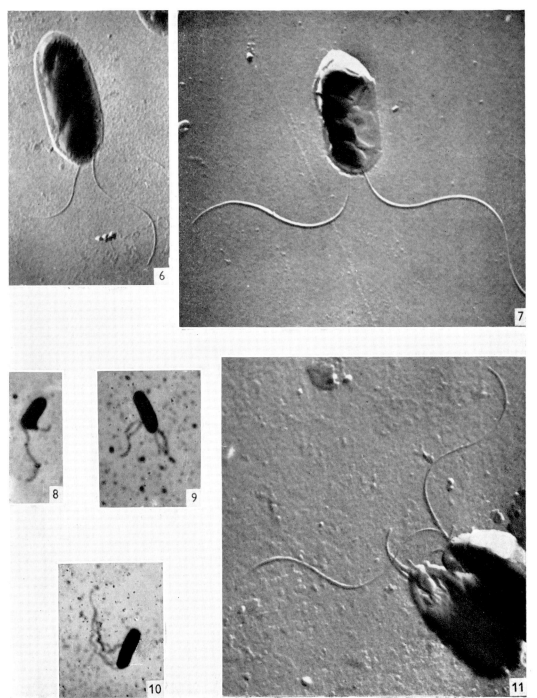

(Reproduced from the Journal of General Microbiology).

Fig. 17

I. SUMMARY

Bacteria possess a cell wall of great strength and rigidity, overlying, and secreted, in certain well-marked areas, by the underlying, semi-permeable cell membrane. Bacteria may be subdivided by cross-walls into a number of cells varying from two to twenty or more. In unicellular bacteria the main growth of the cell wall is at the tips ; in septate forms, the main growth is at the junction of cell wall and cross-walls. These sub-divisions and this mode of growth extends also to the capsule, which may be very complex, with polysaccharide and polypeptide lamina.

The cell wall contains polysaccharide, lipid and protein elements. The chemical composition of the cell wall is more complex in Gram-negative than in Gram-positive bacteria. The cell membrane contains lipid, protein and nucleo-protein elements. It gives rise to the flagella.

In cell division a septum derived from the cell membrane precedes and secretes the cross-wall or ingrowth of the cell wall. These septa and the growing points which secrete the cell wall are basophilic and physiologically active. There is evidence that they constitute a major somatic antigen. They

FIGS. 16 AND 17

DEVELOPMENT OF FLAGELLA

Development of flagella in the germinating microcyst. The resting cells of flagellated bacteria are devoid of flagella ; on germination these develop first at the poles of the cell, especially at the pole remote from the growing point. Electron micrographs, gold-shadowed.

(1, 2, 3, 4) *Salmonella typhi*, stages in the germination of the microcyst.

(1) Microcyst, without flagella. ×30,000.

(2, 4) Young vegetative cells with short flagella concentrated towards one pole of the cell. ×9,000 and ×7,000.

(3) Germinating microcyst with very short flagella towards both poles. ×27,000.

(5, 6, 7) *Bacterium coli*, stages in the germination of the microcyst.

(5) Germinating microcyst with two very short flagella originating at one pole of the cell from an obvious blepharoplast. ×20,000.

(6, 7) Two polar flagella further developed. ×16,000.

(8, 9, 10) Development of flagella demonstrated by silver impregnation stain. ×3,000.

(8) *Proteus*, germinating microcyst.

(9, 10) *Sal. typhi*, very young cells with sub-polar flagella.

(11) Germinating microcysts of *Pseudomonas fluorescens*. The flagella emerge more closely together than in the case of the foregoing examples, which will eventually become peritrichous. Electron micrograph, gold-shadowed. ×16,000.

may also be confused with cellular inclusions and have given rise to a variety of misconceptions.

The cell wall of myxobacteria is flexible and is an organ of motility.

Spore coats resemble the cell walls and may be single or multiple.

The flagella are organs of motility, they are spiral and composed of fibrous protein. They arise from blepharoplasts in the cell membrane. In the germinating microcyst the flagella develop first at the pole remote from the growing point of the cell.

BIBLIOGRAPHY

(1) ANGELICO, R., CALO, A., D'AMORE, A., MARIANI, A., MARIANI-MARELLI, O., SCANGA, F. (1952) Rend. Inst. Sup. di Sanita. 15. 627.

(2) BARTHOLOMEW, J. W. and MITTWER, T. (1951) J. Gen. Microbiol. 5. 39.

(3) BERGERSEN, F. J. (1952) Proc. Univ. Otago Med. Sch. 30. 3.

(4) BIELIG, H. J., KAUSCHE, G. A. and HAARDICK, H. (1949) Zs. f. Naturforschung. 46. 80.

(5) BIRCH-ANDERSEN, A., MAALØE, O. and SÖJSTRAND, F. S. (1953) Biochim. Biophys. Acta. 12. 395.

(6) BISSET, K. A. (1938) J. Path. Bact. 47. 223.

(7) BISSET, K. A. (1939) J. Path. Bact. 48. 427.

(8) BISSET, K. A. (1947) J. Gen. Microbiol. 2. 83.

(9) BISSET, K. A. (1948a) J. Gen. Microbiol. 2. 126.

(10) BISSET, K. A. (1948b) J. Gen. Microbiol. 2. 248.

(11) BISSET, K. A. (1948c) J. Hyg., Camb. 46. 173.

(12) BISSET, K. A. (1949) J. Gen. Microbiol. 3. 93.

(13) BISSET, K. A. (1950a) Exp. Cell. Res. 1. 473.

(14) BISSET, K. A. (1950b) J. Gen. Microbiol. 4. 413.

(15) BISSET, K. A. (1951) ibid. 5. 155.

(16) BISSET, K. A. (1952) Bacteria. Edinburgh. Livingstone.

(17) BISSET, K. A. (1953a) Nature, Lond. 171. 1118.

(18) BISSET, K. A. (1953b) Symp. *Bact. Cytol.* Rome. VI. Int. Cong. Microbiol.

(19) BISSET, K. A. (1954a) J. Bact. 67. 41.

(20) BISSET, K. A. (1954b) Exp. Cell. Res. 7. 232.

(21) BISSET, K. A. and HALE, C. M. F. (1951a) J. Gen. Microbiol. 5. 150.

(22) BISSET, K. A. and HALE, C. M. F. (1951b) J. Gen. Microbiol. 5. 592.

(23) BISSET, K. A. and HALE, C. M. F. (1951c) J. Hyg., Camb. 49. 201.

(24) BISSET, K. A. and HALE, C. M. F. (1953) Exp. Cell. Res. 5. 449.

(25) BISSET, K. A. and MOORE, F. W. (1949) J. Gen. Microbiol. 3. 387.

(26) BOOIJ, H. L. (1949) Dis. Faraday Soc. 6. 143.

(27) BURDON, K. L. (1946) J. Bact. 52. 665.

(28) CASSEL, W. A. (1951) J. Bact. 62. 239.

(29) CHANCE, H. L. (1952) Stain Tech. 27. 253.

(30) CHAPMAN, G. B. and HILLIER, J. (1953) J. Bact. 66. 362.

(31) CHAYEN, J. and NORRIS, K. P. (1953) Nature. 171. 472.

(32) DAWSON, I. M. (1949) Symposium: "The Nature of the Bacterial Surface," Oxford, Blackwell.

(33) DAWSON, I. M. and STERN, H. (1954) Biochim, Biophys. Acta. 13. 31.

(34) DUGUID, J. P. (1951) J. Path. Bact. 63. 673.

(35) EISENBERG, P. (1910) Zbl. f. Bakt. I. 53. 481.

(36) FISCHER, R. and LAROSE, P. (1952). Canad. J. Med. Sci., 30, 86.

(37) GRACE, J. B. (1951) J. Gen. Microbiol. 5. 519.

(38) GRACE, J. B. (1954) J. Gen. Microbiol. 10. 325.

(39) HARRIS, J. E. (1948) New Biology. 5. 26.

(40) HALE, C. M. F. (1953) Lab. Practice. 2. 115.

(41) HENRY, H. and STACEY M. (1943) Nature. 151. 671.

(42) HENRY, H., STACEY M. and TEECE, E. G. (1945) Nature. 156. 720.

(43) HOFFMAN, H. (1951) Nature. 168. 464.

(44) HOLDSWORTH, E. S. (1952a) Biochim. Biophys. Acta. 8. 110.

(45) HOLDSWORTH, E. S. (1952b) Biochim. Biophys. Acta. 9. 19.

(46) HOUWINK, A. L. (1953) ibid. 10. 36.

(47) HOUWINK, A. L. and VAN ITERSON, W. (1947) ibid. 1. 527.

(48) HOUWINK, A. L. and VAN ITERSON, W. (1950) ibid. 5. 10.

(49) HURST, H. (1952) J. Exp. Biol. 29. 30.

(50) ITERSON, W. VAN (1947) Biochim. Biophys. Acta. 1. 527.

(51) ITERSON, W. VAN (1953) Symp. Bact. Cytol. Rome. IV. Int. Cong. Microbiol.

(52) JÄRVI, O and LEVANTO, A. (1950) Acta. Path. Microbiol. Scand. 27. 473.

(53) KINGMA BOLTJES, T. J. (1948) J. Path. Bact. 60. 275.

(54) KLIENEBERGER-NOBEL, E. (1947a) J. Gen. Microbiol. 1. 22.

(55) KLIENEBERGER-NOBEL, E. (1947b) J. Gen. Microbiol. 1. 33.

(56) KLIENEBERGER-NOBEL, E. (1948) J. Hyg., Camb. 46. 345.

(57) KNAYSI, G. (1942) J. Bact. 43. 365.

(58) KNAYSI, G. (1946) J. Bact. 51. 113.

(59) KNAYSI, G. and BAKER, R. F. (1947) J. Bact. 53. 539.

(60) KNAYSI, G. and HILLIER, J. (1949) ibid. 57. 23.

(61) KNAYSI, G., HILLIER, J. and FABRICANT, S. (1950) J. Bact. 60. 423.

(62) KRZEMIENIEWSKI, H. and S. (1928) Act. Soc. Bot. Pol. 5. 46.

(63) LEIFSON, E. (1951) J. Bact. 62. 377.

(64) MARTENS, P. (1937) La Cellule. 46. 357.

(65) MITCHELL, P. (1949) Symposium : " The Nature of the Bacterial Surface." Oxford. Blackwell.

D

(66) MITCHELL, P. and MOYLE, J. (1950) Nature. 166. 218.

(67) MITCHELL, P. and MOYLE, J. (1954) J. Gen. Microbiol. 10. 533.

(68) MORRIS, E. O. (1951a) J. Hyg., Camb. 49. 46.

(69) MORRIS, E. O. (1951b) J. Hyg., Camb. 49. 175.

(70) MORRIS, E. O. (1952) Chem. and Indust. 120.

(71) MUDD, S., BRODIE, A. F., WINTERSCHEID, L. C., HARTMAN, P. E., BEUTNER, E. H. and McLEAN, R. A. (1951) J. Bact. 62. 729.

(72) MUDD, S., WINTERSCHEID, L. C., DeLAMATER, E. D. and HENDERSON, H. J. (1951) J. Bact. 62. 459.

(73) MURRAY, R. G. E. and ROBINOW, C. F. (1952) J. Bact. 63. 298.

(74) PENNINGTON, D. (1949) J. Bact. 57. 163.

(75) PENNINGTON, D. (1950) J. Bact. 59. 617.

(76) PESHKOFF, M. A. (1940) J. Gen. Biol. (Russ.) 1. 598.

(77) PIJPER, A. (1938) J. Path. Bact. 47. 1.

(78) PIJPER, A. (1946) J. Path. Bact. 58. 325.

(79) PIJPER, A. and ABRAHAM, G. (1954) J. Gen. Microbiol. 10. 452.

(80) PRINGSHEIM, E. G. and ROBINOW, C. F. (1947) J. Gen. Microbiol. 1. 267.

(81) ROBINOW, C. F. (1945) Addendum to : The Bacterial Cell. Dubos, R. J. Harvard Univ. Press.

(82) ROBINOW, C. F. (1953) J. Bact. 66. 300.

(83) ROBINOW, C. F. and MURRAY, R. G. E. (1953) Exp. Cell. Res. 4. 390.

(84) SALTON, M. R. J. (1952) Biochim. Biophys. Acta. 9. 334.

(85) SALTON, M. R. J. and HORNE, R. W. (1951) Biochim. Biophys. Acta. 7. 177.

(86) SCHAUDINN, F. (1902) Arch. Protistenk. 1. 306.

(87) SCHAUDINN, F. (1903) Arch. Protistenk. 2. 421.

(88) STACEY, M. (1939) Symposium : " The Nature of the Bacterial Surface." Oxford, Blackwell.

(89) STANIER, R. Y. (1942a) Bact. Rev. 6. 143.

(90) STANIER, R. Y. (1942b) J. Bact. 44. 405.

(91) THORNTON, H. G. and GANGULEE, N. (1926) Proc. Roy. Soc. B. 99. 427.

(92) TOMCSIK, J. (1951) Experientia. 7. 459.

(93) TOMCSIK, J. (1954) Mod. Prob. Paed. 1. 410.

(94) TOMCSIK, J. and GUEX-HOLZER, S. (1951) Schweiz. Zeit. f. Allg. Path. u. Bakt. 14. 515.

(95) TOMCSIK, J. and GUEX-HOLZER, S. (1952) ibid. 15. 517.

(96) TOMCSIK, J. and GUEX-HOLZER, S. (1953) ibid. 16. 882.

(97) TOMCSIK, J. and GUEX-HOLZER, S. (1954a) J. Gen. Microbiol. 10. 97.

(98) TOMCSIK, J. and GUEX-HOLZER, S. (1954b) ibid. 10. 317.

(99) WEIBULL, C. (1948) Biochim. Biophys. Acta. 2. 351.

(100) WEIBULL, C. (1948) ibid. 2. 351.

(101) WEIBULL, C. (1950) Act. Chem. Scand. 4. 268.

(102) WEIBULL, C. (1953a) J. Bact. 66. 137.

(103) WEIBULL, C. (1953b) ibid. 66. 688.

(104) WEIBULL, C. (1953c) ibid. 66. 696.

(105) WONG, S. C. and TUNG, T. (1940) Proc. Soc. Exp. Biol. Med. 43. 749.

CHAPTER IV

The Bacterial Nucleus

A: HISTORICAL

(1, 3, 5, 10, 14, 15, 16, 17, 22, 24, 28, 42, 43, 44, 45, 50, 51, 52, 57, 58, 59)

THE existence of the bacterial nucleus has long been denied, mainly upon the evidence that it cannot readily be demonstrated in preparations fixed and stained according to standard bacteriological procedures (Chapter II). Good descriptions of the nuclear apparatus, as it is now believed to exist, have been published from time to time, but have been ignored by almost all bacteriologists.

It is significant that the observations upon eubacteria, made in the last decade, were preceded by an interest, in widely separated parts of the globe, in the cytology of myxobacteria. These micro-organisms cannot readily be studied in heat-fixed smears, and so received the cytological treatment usually denied to eubacteria. Also their nuclear material can clearly be demonstrated by simple staining techniques, which that of eubacteria often cannot. The application, to other fields of bacteriology, of the information obtained from the study of myxobacteria, gave considerable stimulus to those minds which had difficulty in accepting the defeatist views upon bacterial cytology, which had been current for so long.

A revolution in the study of the bacterial nucleus resulted from the adoption of the technique of acid hydrolysis, as a preliminary to staining. This was originally applied in the process of the Feulgen reaction for nucleic acid, which was used successfully by Stille and by Piekarski in 1937, and by many others at about the same time. Piekarski also discovered that after acid hydrolysis the nuclear structures stained clearly with Giemsa. This technique was adopted by Robinow (1942), whose beautiful photomicrographs attracted

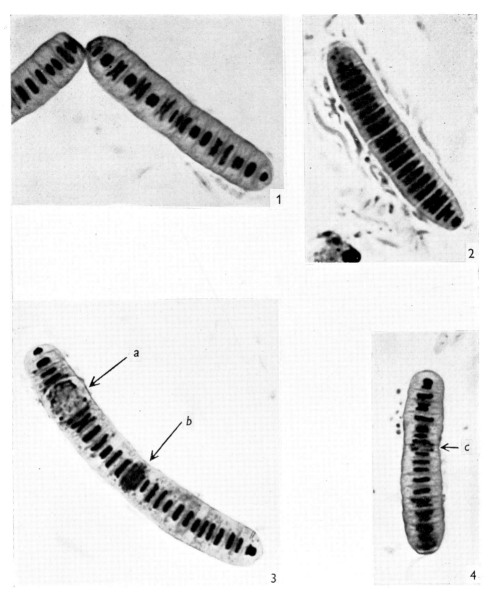

(Reproduced from the Journal of General Microbiology by permission of Mr A. A. Tuffery).

FIG. 18

CYTOLOGY OF OSCILLOSPIRA

Because of its relatively great size, an exceptionally clear picture of the bacterial nucleus is afforded by the giant bacterium *Oscillospira*. In (1) the twin, rod-shaped nucleoids are shown both in profile and endwise. (2) Shows their arrangement within small, disc-like cells. In (3) and (4), *a*, *b* and *c* represent progressively earlier stages in the maturation of the spore and condensation of its nuclear content. (Acid-Giemsa, × 1,000).

considerable attention. Robinow's description of the paired, chromosome-like nuclear bodies was not the first to be made, but was the first to obtain general credence. An easily available but little known paper by Paillot (1919) shows the paired bodies clearly stained by Giemsa, and other examples might be quoted.

Observations were also made by ultra-violet light and by electron microscopy which, if less striking in themselves, served to confirm those made by the acid-Giemsa technique.

Another valuable staining method, the methylene-blue-eosin technique was devised by Badian (1933) and used with success by subsequent workers.

Two interesting studies were performed by a method of vital staining with fuchsin, by Stoughton (1929, 1932) and Allen *et al.* (1939). These papers stand rather apart from the main lines of discovery in this subject, because, although they include observations of great interest, fully substantiated by photomicrographs, the cytological processes described are unlike those more commonly found, in some particulars. These papers will be discussed in Chapters VI and VII.

Claims have from time to time been made to demonstrate a classical mitotic process in the bacterial nucleus, but these have never proved acceptable to experienced bacterial cytologists. Almost without exception they have been based upon an exceedingly small range of observations, and the most recent (DeLamater and Mudd, 1951 *et seq.*) has been supported by the constant (unacknowledged) republication of a single " metaphase spindle," at different magnifications, and sometimes inverted. This work has also been heavily criticised upon technical grounds.

B: THE RESTING NUCLEUS

(2, 4, 5, 10, 11, 12, 13, 18, 19, 20, 21, 25, 26, 27, 31, 32, 33, 34, 35, 36, 40, 41, 42, 47, 50, 52, 53, 59, 60)

The bacterial nucleus, like those of other types of cell, may appear in a variety of different guises. It is probably even more protean than most, but the changes of form which it undergoes are paralleled by similar processes

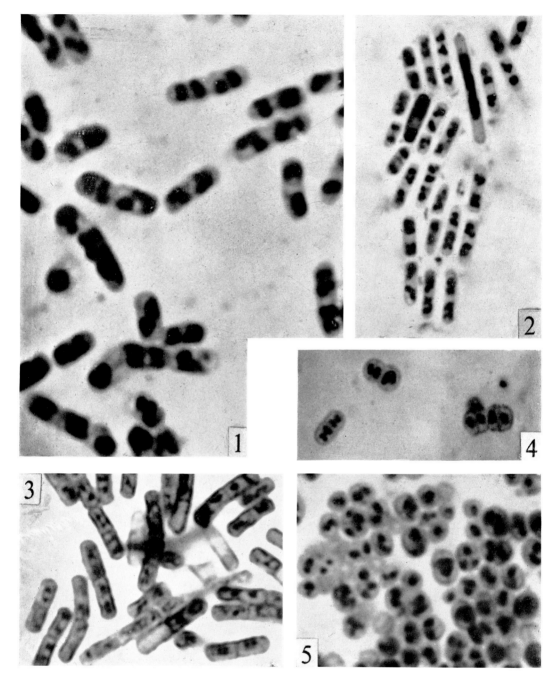

Fig. 19

which have been observed in algæ and fungi, or even in more complex creatures.

The form of nucleus which is usually regarded as the standard equipment of a cell, a roughly spherical, vesicular structure, is found in most bacteria at some stage of their life-history, and in some at all stages. This form of nucleus was not the first to be described in bacteria, nor is it the easiest to demonstrate. Frequently it occurs in resting conditions of the cell, when metabolic activity is low, and the nucleoprotein content, upon which " nuclear " staining reactions depend, is considerably reduced. Hence, in the *Bacteriaceæ*, its presence was undetected for some years after the appearance of the active nucleus, in this type of bacterium, was well recognised.

In those bacteria which possess spherical nuclei in the active condition it is more readily demonstrable, stains clearly and apparently contains its full quota of nucleoproteins. It is found in the active form in some, although by no means all cocci, in the small cells which comprise the bacillary forms of corynebacteria and mycobacteria, and in *Azotobacter*. In the small bacteria it appears spherical and homogeneous, but in *Azotobacter*, which is considerably larger, it may be seen to possess a vesicular structure, consisting of an unstained vacuole surrounded by chromatinic granules. It may be supposed that the same structure would be found in the nuclei of the smaller cells, were it possible to resolve them with the microscope. There is evidence that not all these granules are cytochemically identical.

FIG. 19

THE VEGETATIVE NUCLEUS

The vegetative nucleus of bacteria appears typically in the form of paired rods, dividing reductionally, and usually lying at right-angles to the long axis of the bacterium.

(1-4) Stained by Acid-Giemsa.

(1) *Shigella flexneri,* ×5000.

(2) *Bacillus megaterium,* ×3000.

(3) *Bacillus cereus,* very slightly hydrolysed, showing the relatively small appearance of the nuclei and residual basophilia in the cell envelopes. ×3000.

(4) *Caryophanon latum,* ×3000.

(5) *Micrococcus cryophilus,* a markedly multicellular Gram-positive coccus, with one nuclear body in each cell. These appearances have been confused with mitotic figures by workers unaware of the septate structure of the coccus. Trichloracetic acid and Giemsa, ×5,000.

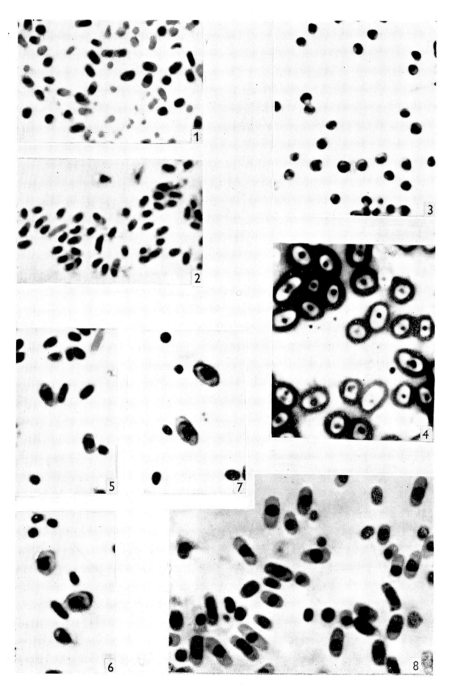

FIG. 20

The nuclei of mycobacteria were described as Feulgen-positive granules, regularly arranged along the length of the bacillus, before it was realised that the bacillus is multicellular, and that each granule was a cell nucleus. Some confusion has also resulted from identification of these granules with those

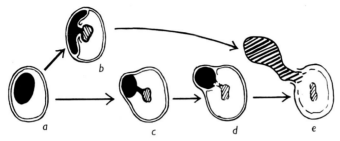

(Reproduced from the Journal of Hygiene).

FIG. 21

EFFECTS OF HYDROLYSIS ON THE SPORE NUCLEUS

a. Spore with nucleus in natural position.

b. The " crescentic nucleus." The nuclear material forms a pool between the cytoplasm and spore coat.

c, d. The " peripheral nucleus." The spore coat is bulged outwards by the ejected nuclear material.

e. Complete ejection of nuclear material.

which appear in the well-known granular or beaded effect seen in heat-fixed preparations of *M. tuberculosis*. The latter are, in fact, merely the shrunken cell contents. The metachromatic granules of *C. diphtheriæ* have also been identified with nuclei by some workers, and disproved by others. They are not seen except in dried preparations, and are artefacts consisting of an aggregate of stainable material within the larger, terminal cells of the bacillus.

FIG. 20

MICROCYSTS OF *BACTERIACEÆ*

The appearance of the resting cell and resting nucleus may be very distinctive, even in bacteria of which the vegetative stages are similar. Acid-Giemsa, $\times 3000$.

(1, 2) *Bacterium coli*. Small, oval cells with an eccentrically staining nucleus. *Proteus* and most *Salmonella* are similar.

(3, 4) *Bacterium aerogenes*, much larger, with a small, central nucleus. ((4) is stained by methylene-blue-eosin).

(5-7) The large microcysts of *S. typhi*.

(8) *Shigella schmitzii*, large oval cells with a central nucleus.

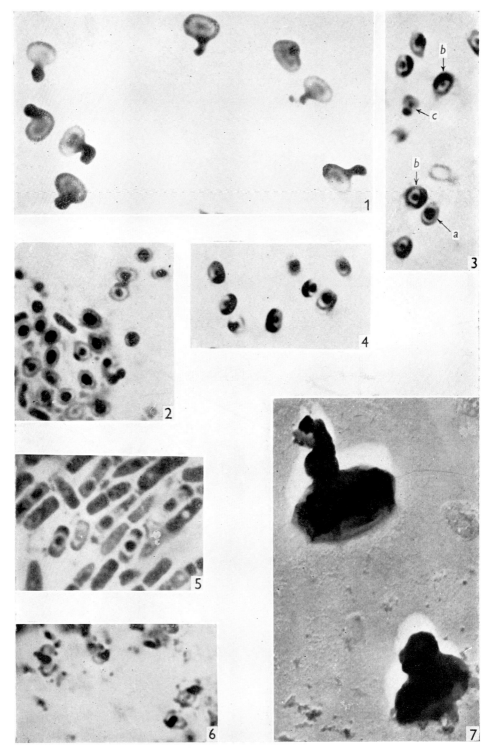

FIG. 22

Coccal genera which possess this type of nucleus may often form short filaments containing four or five nuclei. These filaments are entirely distinct from the reproductive filaments formed by many bacteria, including strepto-cocci, which possess nuclei of the chromosomal type (Sections C and D below).

Where the spherical nucleus is found only in the resting stages of the bacterium it is often more obviously vesicular and stains eccentrically. The main body of the nucleus stains poorly or not at all, and may be difficult to distinguish from the cytoplasm of the cell. The stainable portion of the resting nucleus is sometimes merely a crescentic portion of the outline, but may take the form of a single or double spherical body at one edge. Often this is the only portion of the nucleus which can be resolved, and the appearance is of a small, double, spherical nucleus lying eccentrically in the cell. In the case of myxobacteria and cytophagas the stainable portion may be tadpole-shaped.

The spore nucleus resembles other resting nuclei, but appears to be in a condition of turgour (possibly due to concentration of the protein materials, Chapter IX). The effect of acid-hydrolysis is to weaken the spore-coat, so that the nuclear material may be forced from its natural position to lodge as a pool of basophilic material at the periphery of the cell. The appearances

---

FIG. 22

THE SPORE NUCLEUS

The bacterial endospore has a vesicular resting nucleus, typical of such nuclei, except that it appears to be in a condition of turgour when mature. Under the influence of acid-hydrolysis processes the nuclear material may be partly or completely ejected, giving the various appearances which have, in the past, been described as " peripheral " or " crescentic " nuclei. The immature spore nucleus does not behave in this fashion. The weak spot, through which the nuclear material may be ejected, possibly represents a germination pore.

(1) Spores of *Bacillus sp.*, treated with N/1 nitric acid for 5 minutes, stained Giemsa and re-stained tannic-acid-violet, to demonstrate that the ejected nuclear material is outside the spore coat. One spore has retained it within the spore coat and shows the " peripheral nucleus." ×5000.

(2) Spores of *B. subtilis*, showing the spore nucleus in its natural condition. Acid-Giemsa. ×3000.

(3, 4) Spores of *Clostridium welchii*. Nitric acid for 10 minutes, stained crystal violet. All types of appearances seen ; *a*, nucleus in natural condition ; *b*, " crescentic nucleus " ; *c*, " peripheral nucleus." Other spores are in intermediate stages. ×3000.

(5) Maturing spores of *Cl. welchii*, as in (3, 4), showing no change of position of nucleus.

(6) As (1), after several hours hydrolysis.

(7) As (1), electron micrograph, gold-shadowed. ×16,000.

resulting from this reaction have been variously described as " extracyto-plasmic," " peripheral " or " crescentic " nuclei, but they are now generally agreed to be artefacts.

The identity of the spherical nucleus, as found in active cultures of some genera, with that which is confined to the resting stages of most types of bacteria, whose active nucleus is chromosomal, is not certain. Bacteria, whose active nucleus is spherical but small, may possess a resting nucleus which is larger and more obviously vesicular (Chapter VI).

In the cells of most classes of living organism the nucleus returns from the chromosomal to the resting condition between each division, but in bacteria the mitotic condition of the vegetative cell may be retained throughout the period of active reproduction, and the resting nucleus is restored only when active reproduction ceases. The active condition of the nucleus is so much more readily demonstrable that it has been supposed that the nuclear material preserved an organised form only in young cultures, and became disintegrated and distributed throughout the cytoplasm when cultures were more than a few hours old. This, however, is a fallacy.

FIG. 23

APPEARANCES OF THE NUCLEUS

(1)   Vesicular vegetative nucleus in a Gram-negative coccus. Methylene-blue-eosin.

(2)   False appearance of vesicular nucleus in multicellular coccus. Actually the nuclear material of several cells is condensed centrally. Methyl-violet-nigrosin.

(3)   As (1) in *Sarcina* sp.

(4), (5)   Nuclear bodies in *Mycobacterium lacticola* and in *Nocardia* sp. These appear spherical, but this may be because they are too small to be resolved.

(6)   Appearance of vesicular nucleus in acid-hydrolysed cells of *Aerobacter* sp., probably due to laking of the stain.

All plates at × 3000.

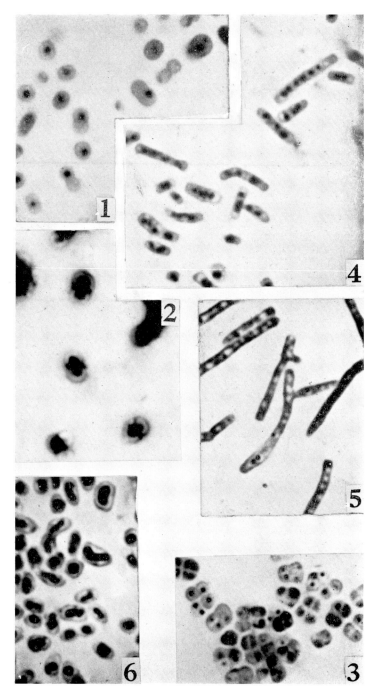

F<small>IG</small> 23

C: THE PRIMARY VEGETATIVE NUCLEUS

(5, 6, 7, 9, 10, 12, 14, 27, 30, 32, 33, 38, 43, 44, 45, 46, 48, 50, 51, 52, 60, 61)

In the young cultures of most eubacteria, myxobacteria and such chlamydo-bacteria as have been described, as well as in the primary mycelium of strepto-myces, the nucleus is found in what is sometimes described as the primary form. It consists of a pair of short rod-like bodies, sometimes slightly broader at the ends than the centre, lying transversely to the long axis of the bacterium, and occupying almost its entire width. They are termed chromatinic bodies or chromosomes, although their exact identity with the chromosomes of plant and animal cells is dubious. They divide with the cell, splitting longi-tudinally in the manner of chromosomes. In consequence of this mode of division the pairs may lie parallel to one another or at a slight angle. They are sometimes so close together as not to be resoluble separately by the microscope, and sometimes quite widely separated. The chromosomes were originally described as single, spherical bodies, and this description is still applied to their appearance in electron micrographs, and by ultra-violet light.

Although the bodies appear rod-shaped, they show a marked tendency to present the long axis of the rod to the observer, so that it has been suggested that they are, in fact, disc-shaped or in the form of a short, spiral band. This is to some extent supported by the observed form of the nuclei of the large micro-organism *Caryophanon latum*, which resembles bacteria in many of its morphological attributes. Its nuclei are ring or disc-shaped, and lie, as a rule, in a plane transverse to the long axis of the bacillus-like organism. An even more remarkable demonstration of a primary vegetative nucleus in the form of unequivocal transverse rods is given, however, by *Oscillospira*, another member of the same group, and even larger than *Caryophanon*. The con-sensus of opinion is that the chromatinic bodies are, as they appear to be,

Figs. 24 and 25
SECTIONS OF BACTERIAL NUCLEI

Electron micrographs of ultra-thin sections of *Bacterium coli*. The material has probably suffered some distortion in the process of fixation in osmium tetroxide solution and embedding in synthetic resin, but nevertheless shows the absence of cross-walls in this type of bacterium, and the nuclear bodies in the form of short rods in both longitudinal and transverse sections. Exactly as in stained preparations, the nuclei appear singly or in pairs towards each end of the cells, or in larger numbers in the filaments.

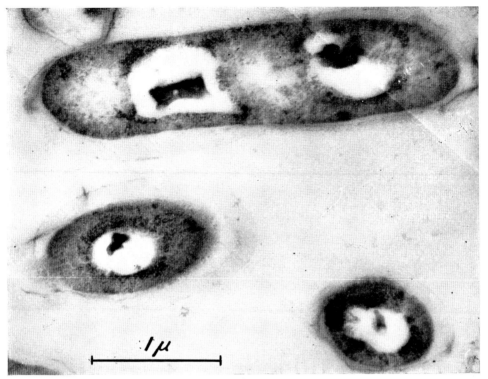

FIG 24

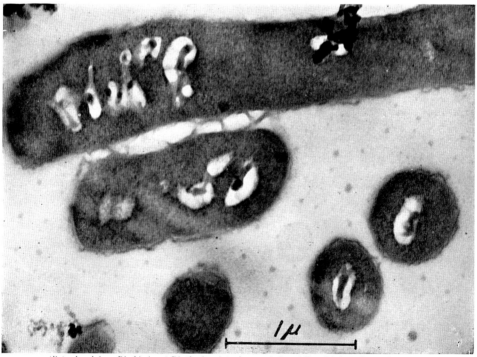

(Reproduced from Biochimica et Biophysica Acta, by permission of Drs. Birch-Andersen, Maaloe and Sjöstrand).

FIG 25

short rods. And in fact they occasionally appear as though viewed from the end, although not so frequently as might be expected in such a case. The figures of Robinow and Klieneberger-Nobel occasionally show the pairs of rods crossed. In the experience of the author this is exceedingly uncommon, but if the chromosomes are in fact rods there is no theoretical reason why they should not appear crossed. Genetical evidence also supports this concept of a reductionally dividing nucleus (Witkin, 1951).

The slightly dumbbell-shaped appearance of the chromosomes is usual, although not invariable. It is not indicative of division in the transverse plane, as might, perhaps, be expected. Division of the chromosomes is invariably by longitudinal splitting, and it is obvious that if these bodies carry the genes of the cell, arranged in a linear manner, as from genetical considerations must necessarily be true, then their division cannot take place in any other way.

The nuclear unit of the vegetative cell is a single pair of chromosomes. In bacteria of unicellular, smooth morphology a pair is disposed at each end of the cell, but it is probable that both pairs are of identical genetical constitution (Chapter X). In very young cultures of bacteria of this morphology the cells often contain only a single pair of chromosomes, and the bacteria may contain from one to four or six cells (Chapter III). Each of the four cells of a rough bacillus contains one pair of chromosomes, but the arrangement of the cells, and the method of cell division in the two, morphological types, are perfectly distinct (Chapter III). It is probable that these multicellular smooth bacteria occur mainly in cultures which are in process of germination.

D: GERMINATION OF THE RESTING STAGE
(27, 30, 31, 32, 35, 36, 39, 55, 61)

The germination of the spore, microcyst or resting cell is accomplished in exactly the same manner in each case. The cell commences to elongate, and in the case of some spores and microcysts, casts the outside wall. The vesicular nucleus is transformed into a single, large transverse rod, which almost immediately divides into two, and afterwards, in the case of smooth types, into four. Normal cell division then commences.

During the process of germination the cell increases in size, except in the case of myxobacteria which tend rather to diminish, the nucleic acid content increases, and the nuclear material becomes large and readily stainable. This is the period of the lag phase of the culture. In the logarithmic phase, which immediately follows, the bacteria at first divide by simple fission alone, but later this method is accompanied by others more complex, and eventually the resting nucleus is restored.

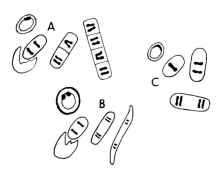

FIG. 26

THE GERMINATION OF THE RESTING STAGE

A. The spore of a rough bacillus.

B. The microcyst of *Cytophaga* sp.

C. The resting cell of *Bact. coli*.

The process is similar in each case. The wall may be shed or absorbed. The vesicular nucleus is transformed into one or more bar-shaped bodies and these divide to give the vegetative nucleus.

E. THE SPHERICAL VEGETATIVE NUCLEUS
(7, 10, 11, 17, 21, 26, 42, 50)

The exact behaviour of the nucleus of the corynebacteria, mycobacteria and cocci at cell division has not been recorded. It appears to be a simple sphere, even when it attains to a size comparable with that at which the double rod-shape of the primary nucleus of eubacteria may distinctly be resolved by the microscope. In the reduction process which precedes the

E

formation of the resting nucleus in *M. tuberculosis* the nuclear material appears in the form of a pair of chromosomes or chromosome complexes (Chapter VI), but these are not normally evident at cell division.

In those cocci which possess a spherical, vegetative nucleus it may be seen to elongate with the cell in the course of division, but the details of the

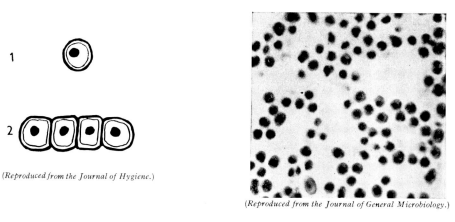

1

2

(*Reproduced from the Journal of Hygiene.*)

(*Reproduced from the Journal of General Microbiology.*)

FIGS. 27 AND 28

THE SPHERICAL VEGETATIVE NUCLEUS

FIG. 27

1. Coccus (not all are of this type).
2. Corynebacterium.

FIG. 28

A unicellular coccus. The nucleus appears to elongate on division. Acid-Giemsa × 3000. (Compare Fig. 7 (12).

process are entirely obscure. Most cocci are multicellular, however, and in some of these, misinterpreted as single cells, entirely spurious " mitotic figures " have been described (*c.f.* Bisset, 1954).

Upon this point as upon others the condition in *Azotobacter*, which because of its larger size may more easily be studied, provides the best available information. The vesicular nucleus of *Azotobacter* undergoes a process which resembles a simple mitosis. The nuclear material becomes concentrated in four chromosome complexes, two of which migrate into each half of the dividing cell and there divide and subdivide, reforming the chromatinic granules which surround the nucleus and which probably represent the elementary chromosomes.

The germination of the cyst in *Azotobacter* is also entirely comparable with the similar germination processes in other bacteria. The vesicular resting nucleus divides into two chromosome complexes and then into the four of the active nucleus, at which stage the cyst is ruptured and the vegetative cell escapes.

F: COMPLEX VEGETATIVE REPRODUCTION
(8, 9, 10, 27, 31, 41, 52)

This mode of reproduction is common, although not invariably present, in many types of bacteria, but does not appear to be found in spore-bearing eubacteria. The nuclear appearances which accompany it are very striking. Filamentous forms are common in films made from such cultures, but in contrast to the filaments which occur in rough cultures, which are multi-cellular, repeating in each unit of the chain the nuclear pattern of the individual, the reproductive filaments are unicellular and their nuclear material is arranged in a distinctive manner. Such filaments may, however, occur in cultures of both smooth and rough morphology, and even in cocci. Although there are recognisable differences between the various types the general plan is similar in all of them. The slightly spiral morphology of the individual bacterium is more clearly shown in these elongated cells, which, because they are curved in two dimensions are difficult to photograph in such a manner as to keep their entire length in focus.

In smooth cultures, the shortest filaments, which are about twice the length of a single bacterium, have their chromosomes packed together at the centre of the cell. Where they can be distinguished separately they are invariably found to consist of three pairs. Filaments of slightly greater length contain six pairs of bodies, which may be together at the centre of the cell, or at a later stage, distributed in pairs throughout the length of the filament. This increase represents a single nuclear division within the fusion cell. A second nuclear division occurs after the chromosome pairs have been

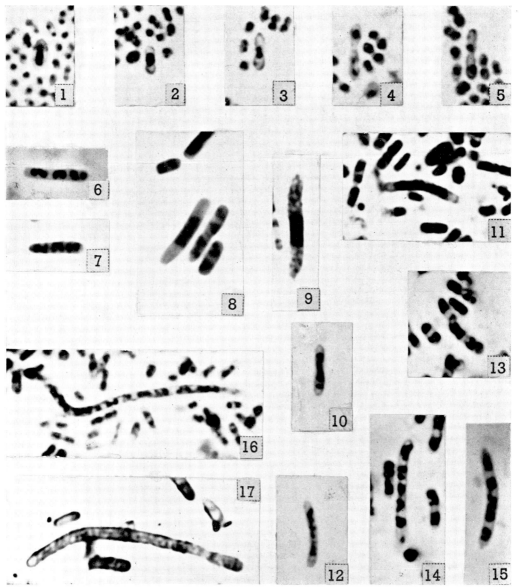

FIG. 29   *(Reproduced from the Journal of Hygiene.)*

COMPLEX VEGETATIVE REPRODUCTION

(1-5) *Streptococcus faecalis,* × 3000 ; (6-17) *Shigella flexneri,* × 3000.

(1) Large cell with elongated fusion nucleus.

(2-4) Development of filament.

(5) Fragmentation of filament.

(6, 7) Trinucleate pre-fusion cells.

(8, 9) Fusion nuclei. In (8) compare fusion cell (*left*) with dividing cell (*centre*) and normal cell (*right*).

(10, 11, 12) Development of fusion nucleus.

(13, 14, 15) Redistribution of nuclear elements in growing filament.

(16, 17) Fragmentation of filament. (16) stained for nuclear structures, (17) for cell walls.

redistributed in the filament, and the latter then fragments into individual bacteria, each containing two pairs of chromosomes. Thus each chromosome of the original six becomes the parent of the entire complement of two pairs in one daughter bacterium. The occurrence of the fusion process has now been confirmed by genetic studies (Section G, below).

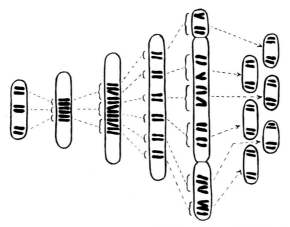

(Reproduced from the Journal of Hygiene.)

FIG. 30

COMPLEX VEGETATIVE REPRODUCTION IN *BACTERIUM*

The trinucleate cell precedes the fusion cell with its three pairs of chromosome complexes, Within the fusion cell there is one nuclear division. The six chromosome pairs are redistributed in the growing filament. There is a second nuclear division and the filament fragments into six daughter cells, each with the full complement of two pairs of chromosome complexes. In streptococci only three daughter cells are formed.

Nothing has been recorded of the process by which the fusion cell which inaugurates this series of changes attains its form and nuclear complement. Bacteria occur which are probably the precursors of the fusion cells, as they contain three pairs of chromosomes, arranged in a more normal manner, with one pair at each end and one in the centre of the bacterium. But how these are derived from a bacterium with two pairs is not easy to understand, and some undetected process of reduction may be entailed.

This method of reproduction, as it occurs in rough bacteria and also in streptococci, is essentially similar to that in smooth bacteria but differs slightly in detail.   The fusion cell of a lactobacillus is approximately the same size as the four-celled rough bacterium, and contains two, large, nuclear bodies.

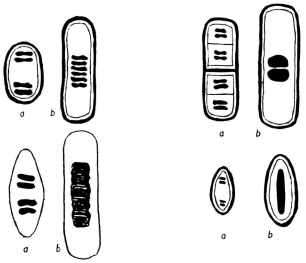

(*Reproduced from the Journal of Hygiene.*)

FIG. 31

THE PRIMARY NUCLEUS AND VEGETATIVE FUSION CELLS
IN VARIOUS BACTERIA

((a) Primary nucleus ; (b) Fusion cell, in each case)
Top left—Smooth bacterium.
Top right—Rough bacterium.
Bottom left—Myxobacterium.
Bottom right—Short-chained streptococcus.

The individual chromosomes cannot be resolved in this case.   The filament increases in length and eventually fragments, exactly as in the case of the smooth types, but the behaviour of the nuclear material is slightly different. The central mass of chromatin retains its identity for some time after the commencement of growth.   Small fragments break off and migrate along the filament, and eventually the chromosome pairs are evenly distributed along its length.   The filament then fragments into bacillary forms ; how many has not been determined.

In the case of *Streptococcus faecalis*, which is a short-chained streptococcus, resembling a smooth bacterium in the possession of two pairs of nuclear units and in its mode of division, by constriction of the cell wall (Chapter III), the fusion nucleus is rod-shaped, with its axis longitudinally disposed in the oval coccus. The rod is transformed into a single, central mass, from which small fragments break off, as in the case of the lactobacillus. The filament which is produced is comparatively short, and gives rise to three instead of

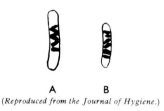

A   B
(Reproduced from the Journal of Hygiene.)

FIG. 32

TRACINGS OF PHOTOMICROGRAPHS OF VEGETATIVE FUSION CELLS
A.   *Shigella flexneri.*
B.   *Bact. coli.*
Showing three pairs of chromosome complexes.

six cells upon fragmentation. The occurrence, in both cases, of a multiple of three, which is the number of pairs of chromosomes in the smooth type of fusion cell, indicates a similarity of constitution of the streptococcal fusion cell.

Filamentous cells, containing chromosome fusions of this type, occur also in myxobacteria and in chlamydobacteria, but the details of the process, as it occurs in these bacterial orders have not been described.

It has been noted that this process does not appear to occur in spore-bearing bacilli. In these organisms, however, there is evidence of a complex method of vegetative reproduction which entails the liberation of small bodies which grow up into bacilli (Chapter VII).

In addition to vegetative cells which resemble those of other, Gram-negative bacteria, cultures of *Proteus* contain swarmer filaments of considerable length, containing a large number of nuclear units. These filaments appear to be unicellular, but their nuclear material is arranged in a simple, repetitive pattern, unlike that of the reproductive filaments.   Their function is distributive and they comprise the swarm.   Evidence has been presented to suggest that these swarmer filaments take part in a reproductive cycle, including the formation of zygospores at the points of contact of swarms.   This interpretation, which is controversial, will be discussed in Chapters VI and VII.

Other types of filamentous cell are common in bacterial cultures.   Some of these contain reduced or disorganised nuclear material.   Their significance is unknown, and they may be pathological.

G: THE NATURE OF THE CHROMOSOME
(9, 10, 38, 39, 42, 48, 50, 51, 52, 54, 60, 61)

It is dubious whether the bacterial chromosome exactly corresponds to that of other cells.   It performs the function of ensuring the correct distribution of genes, which may be assumed to be arranged upon it in a linear manner ; and although in this particular it exactly resembles other chromosomes, it differs from them in a number of respects.   It is actually less susceptible than the resting nucleus to radiations (Rubin, 1954), and being single, it does not require an elaborate mitotic process to ensure correct distribution.

Early genetic studies upon certain bacteria led to the adoption of theories requiring the existence of three chromosomes or even of a branched chromosome ; but more recently it has been established that genetically, as well as cytologically, a single chromosome must be assumed.

In the process of fission it appears that each member of each pair of chromosomes is identical with the others, and is in fact derived from the same parent chromosome in previous cell generations.   This is quite unlike the condition in plant or animal cells, where the two members of the pair may be of entirely different constitution with respect to several genes.   Similarly, when a smooth bacterium divides, the chromosome pair at one end of the cell passes into one daughter cell, and the pair at the other end, into the other daughter cell. Thus the entire complement of four chromosomes is derived, at a remove of two cell divisions, from a single, " grandparent " chromosome.   Or at a remove of two nuclear divisions, with or without cell division, in the case of the fusion-fragmentation method of reproduction. While the truth of this interpretation cannot be established with certainty until technical methods permit the accurate identification of individual chromosomes, or else enable the process of nuclear division to be followed in the living cell, it is certain that the appearance of fixed and stained material, at different stages of the process, does not encourage any other interpretation. It may be argued that this method of study is unreliable, but it was until recently the only method by which the nuclear processes accompanying cell division could be studied in all types of cell; these processes have recently been examined by the technique of phase-contrast cinematography, with the result that the earlier interpretations have in most respects been most admirably verified. But the most remarkable vindication of the now classical observations of bacterial cytology is the manner in which genetical work has, quite independently, confirmed every conclusion after a greater or lesser delay.

A complete distribution of nuclear material, on the lines of mitosis in higher types of organism, could only occur if it were possible for the halves of the newly-divided chromosomes to slip past one another and occupy a position in the opposite half of the dividing cell. Not only is there no evidence that this may occur, except the rather doubtful figures of crossed chromosomes referred to previously, but the genetical evidence entirely supports the concept of a reductional chromosome division. Supposed classical mitotic figures, which have been claimed to be demonstrated in bacteria cannot be taken seriously.

It follows, therefore, that although bacteria may commence their life, in a particular culture, with a set of two or four chromosomes of different genetic constitution, possibly derived from the sexual processes which appear to precede the formation of the resting nucleus, these differently constituted chromosomes will rapidly become segregated, without the intervention of further sexual conjugation. It appears that the vegetative generations of bacteria of this type are haploid, but sometimes multinucleate, a conclusion which is borne out by genetic studies (Chapter X). The multinucleate condition is irregular, bacteria in the same culture may have one, two, four or more chromosome-like nuclei.

It was shown by Witkin (1951) that if bacteria which produce easily recognisable variant colonies are irradiated at a stage of growth when the majority of cells have a single chromosome, then complete variant colonies are produced. If they have two or four chromosomes then sectored colonies, with half or quarter variant sectors respectively, are produced. The segregation of the variant character, produced by alteration of an irradiated chromosome, takes place after a delay of two vegetative divisions, representing the process

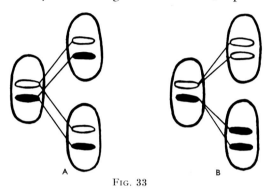

FIG. 33

FATE OF CHROMOSOMES IN CELL DIVISION

A. Equational division. This does not occur in bacteria. Even if the occurrence of a classical mitosis (for which there is no reliable evidence) were accepted, it would entail migration of chromosomes across their own partners and across the newly-formed cell division.

B. Reductional division. This appears to be the normal condition in bacteria. It was originally postulated by cytologists (*e.g.* in the first edition of this book), but is now supported by genetical evidence also (*e.g.*, Ryan, F. J. and Wainwright, J. K., *J. Gen. Microbiol.*, **11.**364). Thus the vegetative cells are haploid but multinucleate, and mutant characters are rapidly segregated.

of nucleur segregation described above. Filamentous cells, derived from the vegetative fusion process, behave as if they possessed a single chromosome ; an observation which confirms the occurrence of a fusion process.

The nucleus of *Azotobacter* resembles that of yeasts in the possession of a number of chromatinic granules which appear to be attached to the nuclear membrane. In the case of yeasts these granules are believed to be the chromosomes. In mitosis these chromosomes take part in the formation of two ribbon-like complexes. In *Azotobacter*, the nuclear material at cell division takes the form of two or four large rods, which divide with the cell and then fragment to reform the vesicular nucleus with its surrounding granules.

A pair of chromosomes or chromosome complexes take part in the meiotic, reduction process which follows nuclear fusion in *M. tuberculosis*. The cells of the vegetative bacillus contain small, spherical nuclei, and the zygote a large, vesicular one. It must be concluded that the difference between the

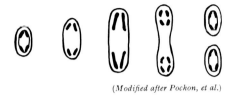

(*Modified after Pochon, et al.*)

FIG. 34

NUCLEAR DIVISION IN *AZOTOBACTER*

The vesicular nucleus reforms as four large chromosome complexes, two of which pass into each half of the dividing cell. Here they divide and reconstitute the vesicular nucleus in each daughter cell.

condition in those bacteria which appear to possess a spherical, vegetative nucleus and those in which the chromosomal condition is obvious and semi-permanent, lies in the power of the former to resume the resting form of the nucleus between each cell division, a state of affairs which is normal in most organisms.

H: THE SECONDARY NUCLEUS

(13, 41, 42, 45, 46, 48)

The secondary type of bacterial nucleus was first described in an interesting paper by Stoughton (1929), and later, independently by Piekarski (1937) who contrasted it with the primary form, but it has been little studied. This is in part explained by the fact that Stoughton failed to demonstrate the primary nucleus by the technique which he employed, so that his findings were not correlated with the later observations upon this phase of the nuclear cycle, whereas Piekarski, although successful in demonstrating both types of nucleus by the Feulgen reaction and by the acid-Giemsa technique as well as by ultra-violet light, failed to resolve them properly, and figured them as spherical bodies, which cast doubt upon the value of his morphological interpretations when the true form of the primary nucleus was afterwards discovered. In fact the morphology of the secondary nucleus is considerably less easy, than that of the primary nucleus, to define. It consists of a structure which, although it may appear single is probably always paired and is disposed centrally in the bacillus. It does not stain with the same clarity as the primary

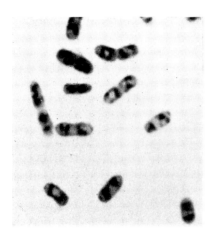 

(Reproduced from the Journal of Hygiene.)

FIG. 35

THE VEGETATIVE NUCLEUS IN *BACT. COLI*

Left—Primary form.
Right—Secondary form.
Acid-Giemsa × 3000.

nucleus, so that its exact form is difficult to determine. It divides with the cell, and has been observed to do so by dark-ground illumination.

The secondary nucleus is an alternative form which may or may not be adopted in the later vegetative stages of a culture. If it is not adopted the nucleus may take the form of a central, chromatinic rod, and thereafter proceed to the formation of the resting nucleus, but the resting stage may also be derived from the secondary nucleus. It has not been recorded as occurring in spore-bearing genera, which pass directly from the primary nuclear phase to the changes associated with sporulation (Chapter VI).

The secondary nucleus was described by Piekarski as a single, spherical nucleus, situated at the centre of the bacterium, in contrast to the primary nuclei, which he described as similar, spherical bodies disposed at each end of the cells which he studied ; a smooth culture of *Salmonella typhi*. Stoughton described it as a single or double structure, not unlike a pair of primary chromosomes, although broader. The organism which he studied, a plant pathogen, formed the resting stage, a spherical body, by a rather unusual method from the secondary nucleus (Chapter VI). By Stoughton's technique, a " vital " staining method, using carbol fuchsin, young cultures of this bacterium stained uniformly, whereas the nuclear structures of older cultures were clearly visible. This was almost certainly due to the masking effect of

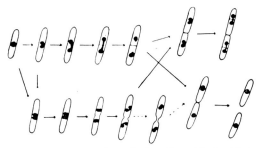

(*After Stoughton. Reproduced from the Proceedings of the Royal Society.*)

FIG. 36

THE SECONDARY NUCLEAR PHASE IN *BACT. MALVACEARUM*
Postulated alternative methods of division.

the ribonucleic acid in the cell membrane of the young cultures (Chapter II).

Bacteria in the secondary nuclear phase often produce forms which appear to be in process of sexual conjugation. They are attached end to end, usually at a slight angle, with the nuclear material concentrated at the point of contact. From such forms Stoughton described the formation of a spherical body resembling the microcyst of myxobacteria. When the resting nucleus is produced from similar forms in *Bact. coli* the process differs from that found in Stoughton's bacterium, which he describes as extruding the spherical body from the point of conjugation, or from the side of a bacterium, whereas in *Bact. coli* the maturing or conjugating cells are transformed directly into microcysts.

The exact relationship between the primary and secondary phases of the nucleus is not clear. The latter may be no more than the result of a reduced rate of nuclear division in the latter stages of a culture, bringing about a restoration of the condition found in very young cultures of smooth bacteria, in which many cells contain only a single pair of chromosomes. Alternatively it may represent a reduced or simplified condition of the nucleus, in preparation for the formation of the resting nucleus.

The secondary nuclear phase is usually found in the latter stages of rough cultures of *Bacteriaceæ*. The filamentous type of growth may be preserved but the cells become more elongated until eventually the unit bacilli are unicellular, and similar to the secondary stage in smooth cultures. The difference between the primary and secondary phases of the nucleus is less in the case of rough than of smooth cultures, because the rough cultures usually have only a single pair of chromosomes in each cell in the primary phase also.

Lactobacilli, however, which are normally of rough morphology, may pass directly from the primary to the resting state of the nucleus. Each of the four cells of the vegetative bacillus is transformed into a microcyst.

I: THE ROD-LIKE NUCLEUS

(3, 13, 14, 20, 27, 30, 31, 32, 33, 36, 56, 57)

The appearance of the bacterial nucleus in the form of a longitudinal, chromatinic rod has frequently been reported, although considerable doubt has been cast upon the significance of this appearance. Lewis (1941), in a review of bacterial cytology, expressed the opinion that the central rod or " spiral " nucleus was, at least partially, an optical illusion, due to the accumulation of unstainable, reserve food materials, and especially fat globules, in the cell. Lewis considered that this resulted in the compression of the remaining stainable cytoplasm into a three-dimensional reticulum, the greatest thickness of which, viewed through the middle of the cylindrical cell, gave the appearance of an irregular, central, chromatinic rod. While it would be rash to assert that this condition never arises, it is unquestionable that the bacterial nucleus frequently assumes a rod form, and it is a regular part of those sexual processes in bacteria which have been most fully described. Its form is often such as to suggest that it is no more than the natural appearance of a mass of amorphous material, nuclear or otherwise, lying within an elongated cell. That this is not so, however, is attested by the retention of the rod form by that portion of the nucleus which is included in the spore of *Clostridium tetani*, during the initial stages of the process of maturation.

Bacterial cells in this nuclear phase are still capable of vegetative reproduction. Gram-negative, intestinal bacteria may adopt the condition in cultures not more than a day old, although they do not invariably do so, as it is alternative to the secondary nuclear phase, which is often found in such circumstances.

The entire secondary mycelium of streptomyces, from which the spore-bearing hyphæ arise, contains rod-shaped nuclei, and they are frequently found in the early stages of sporulation in *Bacillus* and *Clostridium*, although it is uncertain whether, in this case, vegetative reproduction may still be in progress.

Although rod-shaped nuclei are usually found to be associated with sexual conditions in bacteria, their significance is not always the same, as some forms may precede and others succeed conjugation. In the case of the *Bacteriaceæ*, the secondary nucleus or the rod-shaped form, either of which may be found in the later, vegetative stages of the culture, are both capable of giving rise directly to the mature, resting nucleus by an apparently sexual or autogamous process. The rod is often obviously granular, and it is possible that the granules may represent the elementary chromosomes in an alternative arrangement, although they are too small for their behaviour at cell division to be observed.

In streptomyces and spore-bearing bacilli the rods appear solid and consistent, giving no clue as to their composition. A very early study by Schaudinn (1902, 1903) described the rod, in the process of spore formation. Schaudinn considered that it was formed by a condensation of granular material distributed throughout the cytoplasm. This observation has been regarded as supporting the theory that the bacterial nucleus normally exists in a diffuse form, and the more modern views of its nature have caused doubt to be shed upon the validity of Schaudinn's observations. In fact, however, there is reason to believe that, in the process of transformation from the primary condition of the nucleus, the chromatinic material may be dispersed in the form of an, apparently, disorganised mass of granular material from which the rod-like nucleus is reformed. These granules may be identical with those which, in some cases, can be discerned in the completed rod.

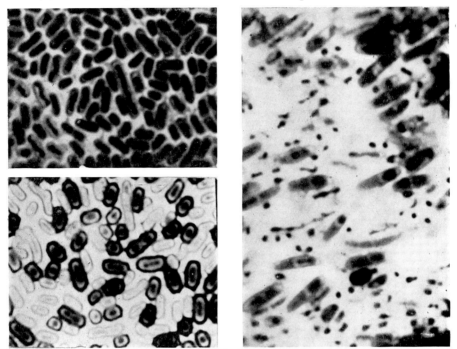

(Reproduced from the Journal of Hygiene and Journal of General Microbiology.)

FIG. 37

TYPES OF ROD-LIKE NUCLEUS

Top Left—Early stages in the maturation of the resting nucleus in *Bact. coli.*

Bottom Left—Similar stages in *Bact. ærogenes* (the dark surface material is capsular)

Right—Rod-forms enclosed in the developing spore of *Cl. tetani.*

Acid-Giemsa × 3000.

The rod-like nucleus in streptomyces and spore-bearing bacilli is apparently a fusion nucleus and can result from a process of sexual conjugation (Chapter VI).

In non-sporing genera, while the nucleus is in this condition, the length of the individual bacteria is often very variable, and they range from short, almost coccal cells, to filaments of considerable length. Cell-division appears to lack the regularity of other nuclear phases.

In myxobacteria and cytophagas the rod-form of the nucleus is less marked, but the equivalent cytological stages possess what is probably an equivalent structure, in the form of an elongated, oval nucleus.

J: THE FORMATION OF THE RESTING NUCLEUS

(1, 2, 3, 4, 5, 13, 14, 19, 20, 23, 25, 27, 30, 31, 32, 33, 35, 36, 40, 41, 47, 49, 60)

The resting stages of different types of bacteria bear a considerable degree of resemblance to one another, especially in the form of the nucleus. Those which have been examined by cytological methods, and properly described, are the endospore of the *Bacillaceæ*, the microcyst of myxobacteria and cytophagas, the oidial spore of streptomyces and the resting cells of *Bacteriaceæ*, of aerobic and anaerobic *Actinomycetaceæ* and *Mycobacteriaceæ*.

Except for the spores of streptomyces, these structures are not reproductive in function, in the sense that the seeds of plants are reproductive, being designed to disseminate the offspring of a single parent ; except in so far as a bacterial culture, or its equivalent in nature, may be regarded as a reproductive or genetical unit.

The bacterial resting stages are designed for survival. The endospore, however, although highly resistant to inimical agencies, may be primarily a distributive agent (Chapter IX). Most others are presumably armoured mainly against inanition, the most probable adverse factor under natural conditions. Even the endospore is not produced, as has been supposed, as a reaction to adverse conditions, but is often most exacting in its requirements of formation.

The general characters of the resting nucleus have already been described, and it is the cytological processes by which the paired, chromosome-like nucleus of the vegetative cell is transformed into an eccentrically staining, vesicular nucleus, with which we are now concerned.

In all known cases an autogamous or a sexual conjugation appears to be entailed. In the formation of the microcysts of myxobacteria and eubacteria this immediately precedes the maturation of the nucleus, but in streptomyces and spore-forming bacilli it takes place some time previously.

F

In myxobacteria and eubacteria the rod form of the nucleus divides into two halves which fuse again into a central nucleus. In some cases the conjugation appears to be autogamous, the two daughter nuclei recombining within the original cell. In others the cell divides completely and the two halves become gametes.

In rough, sporing bacilli the nuclear units of the four cells combine to form a single, rod-shaped fusion nucleus, from which, after a reduction process, the spore nucleus is derived. In sporing bacilli of smooth morphology the fusion nucleus is formed from the two nuclear units of the cell, and the reduction process differs in detail from that of the rough types.

In streptomyces all the cells of the spore-bearing, secondary mycelium contain similar fusion nuclei, derived by an unusual type of conjugation from the primary mycelium.

In *M. tuberculosis* the vesicular nucleus arises directly from the fusion of two of the small, spherical nuclei.

The details of these sexual processes will be described in Chapter VI.

K: SUMMARY

In resting cells the bacterial nucleus is a spherical or vesicular structure, lying centrally in the cell but often staining eccentrically. It is found in this form in spores, microcysts and the resting stages of most bacteria. A similar type of nucleus is found in the active stages of certain cocci, mycobacteria and other bacteria of similar morphology.

More frequently the vegetative nucleus is in the form of paired chromosomes or chromosome complexes. These are short rods lying transversely to the long axis of the cell. The chromosomes take part in simple vegetative division, in which they split longitudinally, dividing with the cell, and in a complex, possibly sexual, method of division, in which a nuclear fusion is followed by elongation of the bacterium as a filament, redistribution of the nucleus and finally fragmentation to produce a new generation of bacilli.

The distribution of the nuclear material at cell division does not follow the same procedure as in the case of plant and animal cells. Both members of the chromosome pairs are of equal value and one is transmitted to each daughter cell. If more than one pair is present, half the nuclear complement passes to each daughter cell, and each chromosome divides, becoming a pair in the next generation.

Cells in young, smooth cultures contain one pair, latterly two pairs of chromosomes. In older cultures the secondary nucleus, a central body, single or double, is found. Alternatively, the nucleus adopts the form of a longitudinal rod. The resting nucleus may arise from either of these nuclear phases, by an autogamous or sexual process.

Cells in rough bacilli contain a single pair of chromosomes which fuse to form a rod-shaped nucleus prior to sporulation. The entire complement of four cells takes part in the fusion.

Non-sporing, rough bacilli usually adopt the secondary nuclear condition in older cultures, and each cell is separately transformed into a microcyst, with or without sexual fusion.

BIBLIOGRAPHY

(1) ALLEN, L. A., APPLEBY, J. C. and WOLF, J. (1939) Zbl. f. Bakt. II. 100. 3.
(2) BADIAN, J. (1930) Act. Soc. Bot. Pol. 7. 55.
(3) BADIAN, J. (1933a) Arch. f. Mikrobiol. 4. 409.
(4) BADIAN, J. (1933b) Act. Soc. Bot. Pol. 10. 361.
(5) BISSET, K. A. (1947) J. Gen. Microbiol. 2. 83.
(6) BISSET, K. A. (1948a) ibid. 2. 126.
(7) BISSET, K. A. (1948b) ibid. 2. 248.
(8) BISSET, K. A. (1948c) J. Hyg., Camb. 46. 173.
(9) BISSET, K. A. (1948d) ibid. 46. 264.
(10) BISSET, K. A. (1949a) J. Gen. Microbiol. 3. 93.
(11) BISSET, K. A. (1949b) ibid. 3. App. ii.
(12) BISSET, K. A. (1949c) J. Hyg., Camb. 47. 182.
(13) BISSET, K. A. (1950) J. Gen. Microbiol. 4. 1.
(14) BISSET, K. A. (1951) Cold Spring Harbor Symposia. 16. 373.
(15) BISSET, K. A. (1953a) Stain Technol. 28. 45.
(16) BISSET, K. A. (1953b) J. Gen. Microbiol. 8. 50.

(17) BISSET, K. A. (1954) J. Bact. 67. 41.
(18) BISSET, K. A. and HALE, C. M. F. (1951) J. Hyg. 49. 201.
(19) BISSET, K. A., GRACE, J. B. and MORRIS, E. O. (1951) Exp. Cell. Res. 3. 388.

(20) BRIEGER, E. M. and ROBINOW, C. F. (1947) J. Hyg., Camb. 45. 413.

(21) BURKE, V., SWARTZ, H. and KLISE, K. S. (1943) J. Bact. 45. 415.

(22) CLARK, J. B., GALYEN, L. I. and WEBB, R. B. (1953) Stain Technol. 28. 313.

(23) DELAMATER, E. D. and HUNTER, M. E. (1952) J. Bact. 63. 13.

(24) DELAMATER, E. D. and MUDD, S. (1951) Exp. Cell. Res. 2. 499.

(25) EPSTEIN, G. W., RAVICH-BIRGER, E. D. and SVINKINA, A. (1936) Gior. di Batt. e Imm. 16. 1.

(26) FLEWETT, T. H. (1948) J. Gen. Microbiol. 2. 325.

(27) GRACE, J. B. (1951) J. Gen. Microbiol. 5. 519.

(28) HALE, C. M. F. (1954) Exp. Cell. Res. 6. 243.

(29) JINKS, J. L. (1954) Bacterial Genetics. Pers. Comm.

(30) KLIENEBERGER-NOBEL, E. (1945) J. Hyg., Camb. 44. 99.

(31) KLIENEBERGER-NOBEL, E. (1947a) J. Gen. Microbiol. 1. 33.

(32) KLIENEBERGER-NOBEL, E. (1947b) ibid. 1. 22.

(33) KNAYSI, G. (1942) J. Bact. 43. 365.

(34) KRZEMIENIEWSKA, H. (1930) Act. Soc. Bot. Pol. 7. 507.

(35) KRZEMIENIEWSKI, H. and S. (1928) ibid. 5. 46.

(36) LEWIS, I. M. (1941) Bact. Rev. 5. 181.

(37) LINDEGREN, C. C. (1935) Zbl. f. Bakt. II. 92. 40.

(38) LINDEGREN, C. C. and G. (1946) Cold Spring Harbor Symposia. 11. 115.

(39) LINDEGREN, C. C. and MELLON, R. R. (1933) Proc. Soc. Exp. Biol. Med. 30. 110.

(40) MORRIS, E. O. (1951a) J. Hyg., Camb. 49. 46.

(41) MORRIS, E. O. (1951b) ibid. 49. 175.

(42) PAILLOT, A. (1919) Ann. Inst. Past. 33. 403.

(43) PESHKOFF, M. A. (1940) J. Gen. Biol. (Russian) 1. 613.

(44) PIEKARSKI, G. (1937) Arch. f. Mikrobiol. 8. 428.

(45) PIEKARSKI, G. (1938) Zbl. f. Bakt. I. 142. 69.

(46) PIEKARSKI, G. (1939) ibid. 144. 140.

(47) PRÉVOT, A. R. (1953) Symp. *Actino.* Rome. VI. Int. Cong. Microbiol.

(48) POCHON, J., TCHAN, Y. T. and WANG, T. L. (1948) Ann. Inst. Past. 74. 182.

(49) PULVERTAFT, R. J. V. (1950) J. Gen. Microbiol. 4. xiv.

(50) ROBINOW, C. F. (1942) Proc. Roy. Soc. B. 130. 299.

(51) ROBINOW, C. F. (1944) J. Hyg., Camb. 43. 413.

(52) ROBINOW, C. F. (1945) Addendum to : " The Bacterial Cell." Dubos, R. J., Harvard Univ. Press.

(53) ROBINOW, C. F. (1953) J. Bact. 66. 300.

(54) RUBIN, B. A. (1954) J. Bact. 67. 361.

(55) SCHAUDINN, F. (1902) Arch. Protistenk. 1. 306.

(56) SCHAUDINN, F. (1903) ibid. 2. 421.

(57) STILLE, B. (1937) Arch. f. Mikrobiol. 8. 125.

(58) STOUGHTON, R. H. (1929) Proc. Roy. Soc. B. 105. 469.

(59) STOUGHTON, R. H. (1932) ibid. 111, 46.

(60) TUFFERY, A. A. (1954) J. Gen. Microbiol. 10. 342.

(61) WITKIN, E. M. (1951) Cold Spring Harbor Symposia. 16. 357.

CHAPTER V

Reproduction

A: THE GROWTH CYCLE

(8, 11, 20, 21, 24, 25)

THE growth cycle of bacteria, whether in culture or under natural conditions, follows a regular pattern of which the main outlines have long been known, although the underlying chemical and cytological changes have more recently been discovered.

When bacteria are transplanted upon a new medium, suitable for their growth, from an older culture, which has passed its period of active reproduction, there is at first an interval of time, known as the lag phase, in which no numerical increase occurs. The bacteria may increase in size but do not divide. The lag phase lasts from one or two hours to six or seven or longer, after which the logarithmic phase commences. The bacteria reproduce by fission, sometimes at very short intervals, and increase in numbers at an approximately logarithmic rate. Much later, after a period which is a function of food-supply, temperature and the physical conditions in the culture, the rate of growth falls steadily and eventually almost ceases. In the decline phase the numbers may actually decrease, although they usually remain static for a long period.

It has been discovered that the chemical constitution of the cells, and especially their nucleotide content varies according to a similar cycle. Bacteria in aged cultures have a low nucleotide content, which, when they are transplanted to a new medium, rises to a high level during the course of the lag phase and falls off gradually as the culture ages. The nucleotide content thus corresponds closely to the state of activity of the nucleus, and presumably indicates the actual level of nuclear material in the cell.

As already indicated (Chapter IV), the lag phase represents the period of germination of the microcyst. The metabolic activity and nucleotide content of the resting nucleus are both low, but in the young, vegetative cell both are high.

If the medium is inoculated, not with cells from an aged culture, but with those already in the active condition, the lag does not occur. The nuclear material is already in the reproductive phase and no delay is entailed.

B: SIMPLE VEGETATIVE REPRODUCTION
(1, 2, 3, 7, 13, 24, 25)

The enormously rapid increase in numbers, which occurs in the logarithmic phase of a bacterial culture, attests to the efficiency of simple fission as a method of reproduction. This rapidity of growth is, of course, due mainly to the small size of bacteria, and the consequent high ratio of cell surface to volume. Rapid colonisation of a new medium is, nevertheless, assisted by the means of reproduction employed.

The epithet " simple," although habitually employed to describe reproduction by fission, is less accurate, as a description, than once it was believed to be.

Many bacteria are multicellular. Corynebacteria and mycobacteria are composed of from one to a dozen small cells ; eubacteria of rough morphology are normally four-celled, and even cocci may contain two, three or four cells. In these circumstances mere cell division does not provide either increased surface area or wider distribution in the medium unless accompanied by fission of the bacterium. In smooth eubacteria multicellularity is mainly associated with active reproduction, in very young cultures, and is seldom evident in older cultures when it might be expected to be disadvantageous, under conditions of more intense competition for a diminished supply of nutrients. In rough eubacteria the method of septum formation, and filamentous habit of growth (Chapter III) often produces a considerable degree of multicellularity in young cultures although it may also be less pronounced in older ones.

Division can never be truly simple, but must always entail division of the nucleus, the formation of a transverse, membranous septum and the secretion of new cell walls, at the same time as the growth of the cell must itself continue. Complementary to the production of structures peculiar to cell division the entire organism increases in size, extends its membrane and wall, its cytoplasm and nuclear material.

There does not appear to be any considerable difference between the process of fission as it occurs in cultures at different nuclear phases. It is most rapid in very young cultures, in the primary phase, but is more regular in slightly older cultures, where the standard complement of two nuclear units per cell has been achieved. It is often irregular in cultures where the nucleus has adopted the rod-form. In this case the length of the cellular units may be very diverse.

Bacteria possess a marked polarity, and almost invariably divide transversely. This is also true of many cocci, which elongate and divide always in the same plane, although in others, notably the commoner types of staphylococci, each division is at right-angles to the previous one. This results in the production of the typical, grape-like clusters.

Rod-shaped bacteria, growing under adverse conditions, may produce pathological forms which divide in an irregular manner, but this rarely occurs in healthy cultures.

Those genera of stalked caulobacteria in which the stalk is attached laterally to the bacterium divide transversely, in the usual manner, the stalk dividing also. Some of those in which the stalk is terminal have been described as dividing longitudinally. Where this occurs (and it does not always do so, Chapter VIII), there is reason to believe that it is not the polarity of division but the shape of the organism which has changed ; the former short axis having been increased at the expense of the long axis. Between these two extremes are numerous types of intermediate morphology, oval and pear-shaped. On the assumption that the most primitive caulobacteria are those which most closely resemble other bacteria, the terminal stalk and longitudinal fission may have developed as an adaptation to sessile life.

Asexual reproduction by fission is common to most unicellular or simple organisms, and is frequently found to alternate with a sexual process, as it does in bacteria also. Multicellular plants and animals have short-circuited this cycle, to some extent, by the production of specialised sexual cells, upon which alone falls the duty of perpetuating the species. The somatic cells reproduce vegetatively and asexually, but eventually die, whereas the reproductive cells, after a brief vegetative career, may undergo sexual conjugation and survive. In bacteria, which lack this specialisation, all cells alike possess the potential for both vegetative and sexual reproduction, although, as in most other cases, few of the cells which achieve maturity in the resting stage are likely to be transferred from a declining culture to a fresh medium, and serve to initiate a new, vegetative generation.

C: POST-FISSION MOVEMENTS
(1, 12, 23)

Attempts by several workers to study the mechanism of cell division in living bacteria have caused an undue amount of attention to be directed towards an interesting, but quite unimportant artefact, the so-called post-fission movements. The phenomenon was first described by Graham-Smith (1910), who perfectly understood its artificial nature. It has, however, been re-examined by workers who appear to have misinterpreted its significance entirely, and it has also been accorded undue prominence in many elementary text-books, probably in default of more valuable information upon cell division in bacteria.

It is stated that, after division, the daughter bacteria move, with relation to one another, in one of several different and characteristic ways. Smooth forms slip past one another and come to lie side by side ; rough bacilli move as upon a hinge at the point of division, the " snapping " movement ; and others, notably corynebacteria, perform this second movement in an exaggerated form, so that the two halves move round upon one another like the closing of a pocket-knife.

These movements may be observed quite readily, but only under the correct conditions. If bacteria are examined in fluid culture or upon the surface of an agar plate, nothing of the kind will be seen. But if the same bacteria are examined either when set in the thickness of solid medium, or growing between a block of medium and a coverslip upon its surface, then the post-fission movements will become obvious. It was by the employment of these techniques that they were first observed, and while it is entirely accurate to describe bacteria as behaving in this manner, under these conditions, the assumption that they do so under normal cultural conditions is quite unjustifiable. The post-fission movements are merely the result of the growth of the bacteria under conditions of severe mechanical restraint. Smooth bacteria grow and elongate against the pressure of the surrounding medium. When separation is complete, the daughter cells may be forced back again, side by side, by the elasticity of the agar. Rough bacilli remain attached at the point of division, and the filament, constrained in the same manner, is compressed concertina-fashion, bending at the points of division. The division of corynebacteria is more complex and will be discussed in Section E of this chapter. It is sufficient here to say that the centre of the bacillus may be very flexible, by reason of its multicellular structure, and the two halves may remain attached even when forced into an acute angle.

The mechanical constraint which brings about these appearances, by its opposition to the growth of the bacteria, occurs to a very limited degree in growth upon the surface of solid medium, and causes those pale shadows of post-fission movements which contribute to the architecture of bacterial colonies (Chapter VIII).

D: COMPLEX REPRODUCTIVE METHODS
(4, 5, 6, 7, 15, 18, 19)

The most striking of the complex reproductive processes which accompany and supersede simple fission in the later stages of a bacterial culture, is the filamentous growth and fragmentation, to which reference has already been made (Chapter IV), and which occurs in many different types of bacteria, in one of a number of similar forms. Fusion cells appear, containing three pairs of chromosome complexes, in the case of smooth eubacteria, and similar fusion nuclei in other types of bacteria. The fusion cell grows into a long filament, undergoing two nuclear divisions, and eventually fragments into individual bacteria, usually in multiples of three.

As this process includes an appearance of nuclear fusion and reorganisation it may be regarded as sexual, vegetative reproduction. There is not enough evidence to suggest whether the initial fusion, which produces the type of cell containing three pairs of chromosome complexes fused at its centre, is autogamous or truly sexual, but the process is obviously quite different from simple, asexual fission. It is, however, a vegetative process, directed towards the purpose of increasing the number of bacteria in the culture, and not, as in the case of the later sexual fusions, concerned with the distribution and perpetuation of the species. As a method of reproduction it probably is not much less efficient than simple fission, because it does not hinder growth by any serious reduction in the proportion of cell surface to volume, as the formation of a more typical symplasm might do. Some energy must be required for the initial fusion, but this need not necessarily be a great loss, and the disadvantage is presumably outweighed by the advantage of the redistribution of nuclear material.

As the behaviour of the chromosome complexes during simple fission is such as to suggest that a rapid segregation of heterozygotes would probably occur, it is possible that sexual, vegetative reproduction may assist in the redistribution of genetical characters in the culture, prior to the change of nuclear phase which usually follows.

Sexual vegetative reproduction may be found at any stage of culture, but is most common in cultures aged from twelve to forty-eight hours, and may often supersede simple fission almost entirely. Cultures in this condition may develop a macroscopically rough appearance, because of the high proportion of filamentous cells ; but this is transient, and disappears as the culture matures.

In myxobacteria, filamentous cells bearing this type of nuclear structure move actively with the rest of the swarm, and exhibit sufficient co-ordination to enable them to crawl as a unit. There is much more apparent variation in the form of such fusion cells in myxobacteria than in eubacteria, and they are rather less frequent.

In *Sphærotilus natans*, a chlamydobacterium, the form of the fusion cells and their nuclei is similar to that of smooth eubacteria, but their behaviour is not known.

Sexual vegetative reproduction has not been reported in spore-bearing bacilli, but the matter has been so little investigated that it would be rash to suggest that it does not occur in exceptional cases.

In *M. tuberculosis* Lindegren and Mellon (1933) have described the production of nucleated coccal gametes, which conjugated sexually to produce larger coccal bodies. The latter fragmented into tetrads, from which the customary bacilli arose once more. As the unit cell of which a mycobacterium is composed is a small coccal body, this process does not differ in its essentials from sexual, vegetative reproduction in *Bacteriaceæ*. Many similar observations upon mycobacteria are less clear in their inferences because the workers concerned were apparently unaware of the processes which correspond to vegetative fission in bacteria of this morphology.

E: FISSION IN MYCOBACTERIA AND CORYNEBACTERIA
(7, 10, 14, 18, 19, 27, 28)

Mycobacteria and corynebacteria possess a morphology which differs strikingly from that of other rod-shaped bacteria. Bacilli of these genera may consist of a single, spherical or oval cell, or of a dozen or more such cells. Often the terminal cells are much larger than the others, and the contents of such enlarged, terminal cells constitute the metachromatic granules of *C. diphtheriæ*. In the case of *M. tuberculosis* the cells are more usually similar in size, or approximately so, and the beaded appearance of the bacillus in a preparation stained by Ziehl-Neelsen's method is due to shrinkage of the cell contents.

Vegetative reproduction, in bacteria of this morphology, may take place in one of two different ways, which correspond to the simple and complex types of fission in eubacteria, although the resemblance is not exact.

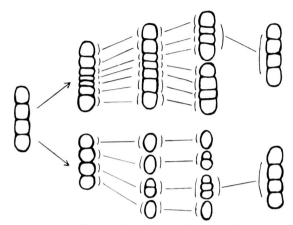

(*Reproduced from the Journal of General Microbiology.*)

FIG. 38

ALTERNATIVE MODES OF DIVISION IN MYCOBACTERIA AND CORYNEBACTERIA

Top—Proliferation of cells, followed by simple fission.
Below—Fragmentation into individual cells, which by growth and division return to the original condition.

In actively growing cultures, rapid cell division takes place at the centres of the bacilli, where the cells become very numerous, without much growth of the bacterium, so that some cells may be reduced to narrow discs, although the terminal cells retain their spherical or oval shape. This multiple cell division is followed by fission of the bacterium. The new, terminal cells,

FIG. 39

THE CYTOLOGY OF CORYNEBACTERIA AND MYCOBACTERIA

(1) *C. diphtheriæ* stained by Neisser's stain, after heat fixation. The " typical morphology " and " metachromatic granules " are seen.

(2), (3), (4) *C. diphtheriæ* stained cytologically for cell walls (by tannic-acid-violet (2)) and for the nuclear structures (by acid-Giemsa, (3), (4)). The bacilli are multicellular, and reproduce in two characteristic ways ; by cell proliferation and simple fission, or by fragmentation.

(5), (6) Similar preparations of a vaginal corynebacterium.

(7), (8), (9) Similar preparations of *M. tuberculosis*. Its structure resembles that of the corynebacteria.

(10) Cell wall stain of *M. phlei*.

All at × 3000.

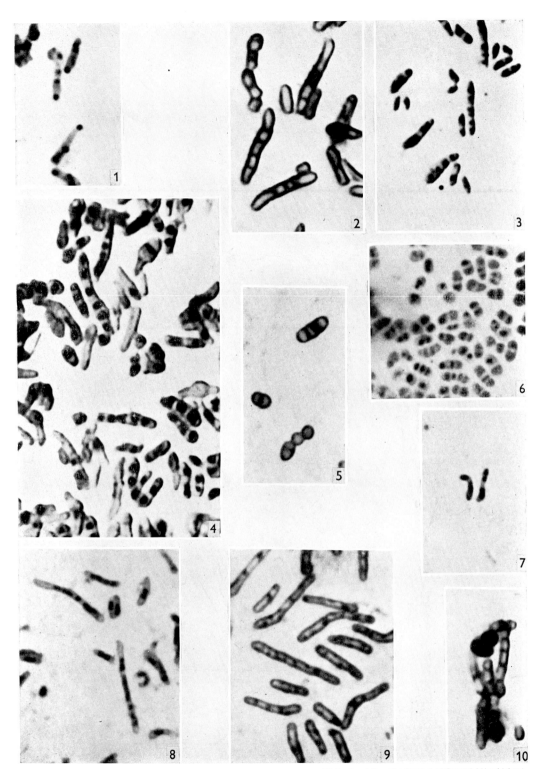

Fig 39

initially small, increase in size, while the central cells continue to multiply rapidly, and the process is repeated. This corresponds to simple fission in unicellular bacteria, and the two processes are not readily distinguishable by routine bacteriological methods.

In mycobacteria the difference in size, between the central and terminal cells is not so great, but the mode of division is otherwise similar.

The alternative method of vegetative reproduction may be found simultaneously, in the same culture, although different strains of bacteria may show a preference for one method or the other. In this case the individual cells grow until they are all spherical or oval in shape. They then separate completely from one another and develop into typical, multicellular bacilli. This is superficially comparable with sexual, vegetative reproduction in eubacteria, but the analogy is by no means complete. There is no apparent sexual process involved, and the filament which fragments to produce the new bacilli is not unicellular, but is a chain of cells, differing only in their larger size from those composing the original bacillus from which the filament arose. It appears, in fact, to be a vegetative process as simple as, or simpler than the first.

Wyckoff and Smithburn (1933) have claimed that the resting stage of M. phlei arises from the fragmentation of the bacilli, and consists of a small, coccal body. But it is not easy to determine from their illustrations whether these workers were concerned with vegetative fragmentation or with the sexual processes which Lindegren and Mellon (1933) showed to precede a more complex mode of reproduction in M. tuberculosis (Section D above). The fragmentation method of reproduction serves, in all probability, to explain a considerable number of reports of complex reproductive cycles in tubercle bacilli, including a filterable stage. Criteria of filterability are purely comparative, but this quality has so often been claimed for M. tuberculosis that it is exceedingly probable that the bacilli may fragment into cells of which a proportion are so tiny as to be capable of passing coarse bacterial filters.

It must, at the same time, be recognised that reproduction by " gonidia," sometimes of filterable dimensions, has been reported in many other species of bacteria (Chapter VII).

F: BRANCHING AND BUDDING

(7, 9, 10, 17, 22, 26)

True branching, as a method of reproduction in bacteria, is confined to the streptomyces. These organisms, which resemble fungi in this as in so many other respects, have elongated cells which take part in the formation of permanent branches. Branching in other bacteria is only occasional, and the

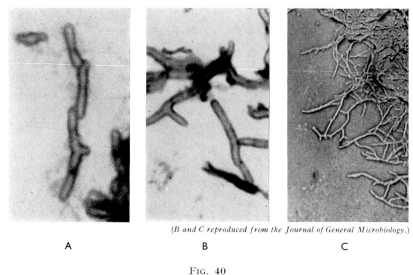

(*B and C reproduced from the Journal of General Microbiology.*)

A   B   C

FIG. 40

BRANCHING IN BACTERIA

A. Branching of the transient, budding type in *C. diphtheriæ*. Tannic-acid-violet × 3000.

B. Somewhat more advanced type of transient branching in a pathogenic actinomyces. Here a true branch may form, but rapidly becomes detached from the main filament. Tannic-acid-violet × 3000.

C. Permanent branching in a streptomyces. Unstained, *in situ* × 1000.

individual cell is seldom or never permanently branched. Branching never occurs in eubacteria and very rarely in mycobacteria. Pathogenic, anaerobic actinomyces, which have little else in common, cytologically, with streptomyces, branch quite frequently, although a good deal less frequently than they have been credited with doing. But the branch does not for long remain attached to the main stem, except in the secondary mycelium.

In these organisms the branch appears first as a small, lateral bud in the cell wall. It elongates, but before it attains to any great size, a septum is formed, dividing it from the parent cell. The branch eventually breaks off at this point and continues to grow as a separate filament. This method of branching is quite unlike that of streptomyces or fungi, in which the mature branch remains attached to the main stem, and in which the cell itself is branched. It more closely resembles the budding of yeasts, and results in the production, not of a stable mycelium, but of an increased number of individual filaments. It may be considered to be a device designed to permit simple, vegetative fission in a filamentous type of bacterium.

This type of branching is also found in "soil diphtheroids." These bacteria have little resemblance to *C. diphtheriæ* but have this, and other characters in common with actinomyces.

Branching in streptomyces is a permanent and integral part of their structure, and it results in the formation of a fungus-like mycelium, which may be regarded as a single organism. Cell division takes place by the production of transverse septa, often at considerable intervals, occasionally close together. True mycelia are not formed by other bacteria. Even in the case of actinomyces and filamentous soil bacteria the mycelium-like tangle of filaments, which may be produced, is in fact a mass of separate, filamentous bacteria. These false mycelia and the true mycelium of streptomyces are both liable to disintegrate into bacillary fragments, and reproduction, in the sense of distribution of the species, may occur from the dissemination of these fragments, as well, in the case of streptomyces, as by the production of spores.

Branching in mycobacteria and corynebacteria is even more transient than in the case of actinomyces, and is confined to a number of specialised strains. It is obvious that microscopic appearances suggestive of branching must be regarded with caution when they occur in bacterial genera which possess so complex a structure, and especially when this structure is not made apparent by standard techniques. Many of the reports of branching in these genera are thus of doubtful value. One of the main exceptions is the avian strain of *M. tuberculosis* described by Brieger and Fell (1945), which branches freely. In this case the appearance suggests that the branch is usually divided from the main stem by a cell wall. Branching is unusual, although not

unknown in human strains of *M. tuberculosis,* but seldom results in the formation of structures more complex than a Y-shaped bacillus. A " branching "
strain of *C. diphtheriæ,* examined by the author, appeared perfectly normal
and unbranched except in very young cultures, where, by ordinary staining
methods, a picture was produced, suggestive of extremely profuse branching.
When stained by cell wall stains, however, the appearance was of masses of
adherent bacilli, and occasional, small, lateral excrescences or buds in the cell
wall. These buds developed, most frequently, in positions where the normal
growth of the cells was obstructed by the adhesion of neighbouring bacteria.
They were probably no more than outgrowths of cells unable to increase in
size by elongation, in the ordinary manner.

It is of some importance that the definition of branching, as a taxonomic
character, should under no circumstances be based upon heat-fixed, Gram-
stained material, nor, preferably, upon the evidence of smears. Whenever
possible, whole mounts of colonies should be used, stained by an appropriate
cytological technique. It is of interest to note that whereas several workers
have described *Streptobacillus moniliformis* as a branched organism, upon the
evidence of heat-fixed smears, van Rooyen (1936) showed, by means of
impression colony preparations (Chapter II), that branching does not occur.
The very frequent use of the epithet " tangled," in qualification of the des-
criptive term " mycelium " is an adequate commentary upon the disinclination
of research workers to differentiate between the natural effects which they
wish to study, and the artefacts which inevitably arise from the mishandling
of biological material.

G: SUMMARY

The lag phase of the growth cycle corresponds to the period of germination
of the microcyst, the logarithmic phase, to the period of nuclear activity, and
in the decline phase the resting condition of the nucleus is adopted. The
nucleotide content of the cell is correlated with these changes in nuclear
activity.

Vegetative reproduction may be asexual or sexual, simple or complex.
Analogous methods of fragmentation and regeneration occur in eubacteria

G

and in the mycobacteria-corynebacteria group, as an alternative to simple fission.   Post-fission movements are artefacts.

Streptomyces form a complex, branched mycelium, but branching in most other groups of bacteria is very rare, and where it occurs it is impermanent and analogous to budding.

BIBLIOGRAPHY

(1) BISSET, K. A. (1939) J. Path. Bact. 48. 427.
(2) BISSET, K. A. (1947) J. Gen. Microbiol. 2. 83.
(3) BISSET, K. A. (1948a) ibid. 2. 126.
(4) BISSET, K. A. (1948b) ibid. 2. 248.
(5) BISSET, K. A. (1948c) J. Hyg., Camb. 46. 173.
(6) BISSET, K. A. (1948d) ibid. 46. 264.
(7) BISSET, K. A. (1949a) J. Gen. Microbiol. 3. 93.
(8) BISSET, K. A. (1949b) J. Hyg., Camb. 47. 182.
(9) BISSET, K. A. and MOORE, F. W. (1949) J. Gen. Microbiol. 3. 387.
(10) BRIEGER, E. M. and FELL, H. B. (1945) J. Hyg., Camb. 44. 158.
(11) GRACE, J. B. (1948) The Cytology of Cytophagas. Pers. comm.
(12) GRAHAM-SMITH, G. S. (1910) Parasitology. 3. 17.
(13) HENRICI, A. T. and JOHNSON, D. E. (1935) J. Bact. 30. 61.
(14) KAHN, M. C. (1930) Tubercle. 11. 202.
(15) KLIENEBERGER-NOBEL, E. (1945) J. Hyg., Camb. 44. 99.
(16) KLIENEBERGER-NOBEL, E. (1947a) J. Gen. Microbiol. 1. 33.
(17) KLIENEBERGER-NOBEL, E. (1947b) ibid. 1. 22.
(18) LINDEGREN, C. C. and MELLON, R. R. (1932) J. Bact. 25. 47.
(19) LINDEGREN, C. C. and MELLON, R. R. (1933) Proc. Soc. Exp. Biol. Med. 30. 110.
(20) MALMGREN, B. and HEDEN, C. G. (1947a) Act. Path. Scand. 24. 437.
(21) MALMGREN, B. and HEDEN, C. G. (1947b) Nature, Lond. 159. 577.
(22) MORRIS, E. O. (1951) J. Hyg., Camb. 49. 46.
(23) NUTT, M. M. (1927) J. Hyg., Camb. 26. 44.
(24) ROBINOW, C. F. (1942) Proc. Roy. Soc. B. 130. 299.
(25) ROBINOW, C. F. (1944) J. Hyg., Camb. 43. 413.
(26) ROOYEN, C. E. VAN (1936) J. Path. Bact. 43. 455.
(27) WYCKOFF, R. W. G. (1934) Am. Rev. Tub. 29. 389.
(28) WYCKOFF, R. W. G. and SMITHBURN, K. C. (1933) J. Inf. Dis. 53. 201.

CHAPTER VI

Sexuality in Bacteria

A: THE EXISTENCE OF SEXUALITY

THE process of sexual fusion is a normal part of the nuclear cycle of most of the cytologically distinct types of bacteria which have been described in the foregoing pages. The mechanism is very similar in each case, and differs in no essential particular from similar processes in algæ, fungi and protozoa. A variety of exceptional methods of sexual reproduction have also been described, but even these are more remarkable for their orthodoxy than for any characteristics which may be considered peculiar to bacteria. This is not a suitable place to discuss the problem of whether bacteria are or are not a homogeneous group, but it is true that, whereas they may be of widely divergent philogeny, the recorded differences in their sexual mechanisms are no greater than may be found in any other, comparable group.

Although the outlines of the sexual cycle, as they appear from cytological studies, are exceedingly well confirmed by such genetical evidence as is available, the entire process of fusion and reduction is not known in every case. The most notable omission is a convincing account of reduction as it occurs in non-sporing eubacteria, in which two distinct types of nuclear fusion have been described, one in the vegetative and one in the resting condition.

B: SEXUALITY IN SPORING BACILLI

(1, 3, 8, 10, 12, 15, 26, 28, 29)

Vegetative sporing bacilli may be of either rough or smooth morphology. The larger species are almost invariably rough and contain a typical arrangement of four cells in the bacillus (Chapter III). The multicellular nature of

99

the bacillus was not clearly observed by some of the cytologists who used bacteria of this type as material for the study of sporulation, and they accordingly described the nuclear fusion, which precedes the formation of the spore, as

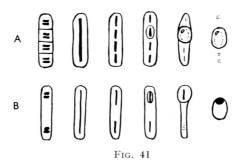

FIG. 41

MATURATION OF THE SPORE

A. Rough bacillus. The nuclear material from the four cells fuses sexually to form a rod-like nucleus. This redivides into four units, of which three are eliminated and one incorporated in the spore. The reduction process.

B. Smooth bacillus. Two instead of four nuclear units take part, both within the same cell. These fuse and then separate ; one is eliminated.

an autogamous process. As it entails the fusion of nuclear material from more than one cell, however, it may reasonably be considered to be sexual. In the case of sporing bacilli of smooth morphology, which are unicellular but possess two nuclear units in each cell, the fusion between these two units can only be regarded as autogamous, unless it can conclusively be proved, as

FIG. 42

THE MATURATION OF THE SPORE

(1) *Clostridium welchii*, vegetative cells, acid-Giemsa × 2800.

(2) *Cl. welchii*, nuclear fusion, acid-Giemsa × 3500.

(3) *Cl. welchii*, fusion cells, acid-Giemsa × 3500.

(4) *Cl. welchii*, maturing sporangia, acid-Giemsa × 1875.

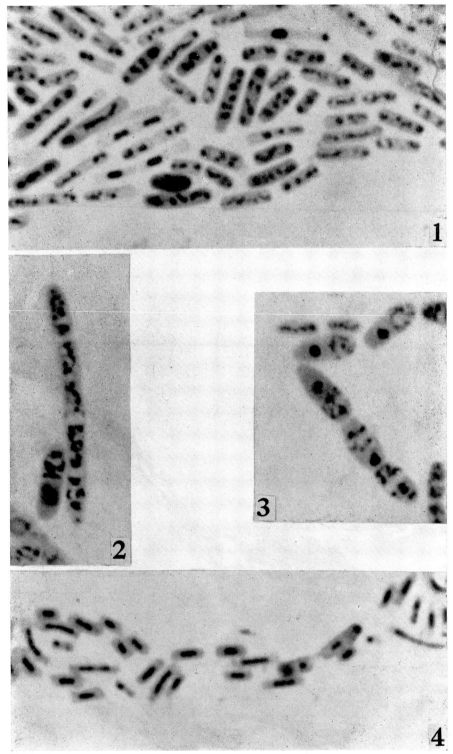

(*Photomicrographs by Dr. E. Klieneberger-Nobel. Reproduced from the Journal of Hygiene*).

FIG 42

claimed by Schaudinn (1902-03), in the earliest cytological study of sporulation, that the fusion is preceded by a partial cell division. This point is not clearly established by the available evidence. Klieneberger-Nobel (1945) claims that cell-division occurs *after* fusion, but this must be regarded as the production of a diploid, vegetative generation, such as occurs, more elaborately, in streptomyces. It is not a reduction division, as this occurs at a later stage.

The nuclear material derived from the four cells of the rough bacillus, or from the two nuclear units of the smooth cell, forms a longitudinal, rod-shaped fusion nucleus (Chapter IV). In both cases the unit which forms the zygote and produces the spore is the bacillus, whether unicellular or otherwise. This is not true of the formation of the resting nucleus in rough eubacteria, or in *M. tuberculosis*, in which the unit is the cell (Chapter IV and Sections D, E, F below). The fusion nucleus then divides into four short rods, in the case of rough bacilli, and two in the case of the smooth bacilli. These rods appear to represent the nuclear units taking part in the fusion. One rod is enclosed in the developing spore, which appears as a clear area of cytoplasm, bounded by an obvious spore wall. The remaining one or three nucleoids are rejected. They may be absorbed into the cytoplasm or may be discarded upon the dissolution of the sporangium, which follows the maturation of the spore. This constitutes the reduction process, and is reminiscent of the elimination of the polar bodies in mammalian oogenesis.

The longitudinal rod form of the nucleus may be retained for a short time in the maturing spore, but eventually a typical, eccentrically staining, resting nucleus is produced.

The spore is thus haploid, and the vegetative generations which arise from it are similarly haploid. The diploid generations are those which occur between the sexual process and the production of the spore. They are probably few in number.

A second and more detailed account of the reduction process in sporulation is given by Allen *et al.* (1939). It differs from that agreed by most other workers, but as it is well substantiated, may represent a parallel method, less commonly found. The bacillus studied by these workers produced nuclear figures, immediately before the production of the spore, which resembled classical meiosis as it occurs in plant and animal reproductive cells. The details of the sexual fusion which presumably preceded this process were not recorded, but the remarkable cross-like figures of the meiotic division are clearly illustrated in photomicrographs. It is unfortunate that the " vital " staining technique used in this study was capable of demonstrating these structures, but not the rest of the cytological processes which must undoubtedly have occurred in the same organism.

C: SYNGAMOUS VEGETATIVE REPRODUCTION

(6, 7, 14, 25)

In this section and the next the sexual processes of eubacteria and myxobacteria will be discussed together. The cytology of myxobacteria was known long before that of eubacteria, but the two are entirely similar in so far as the behaviour of the nucleus is concerned. The vegetative cells, which have already been discussed, may undergo what appears to be an autogamous process, in the course of a method of reproduction alternative to simple fission (Chapters IV and V). The mode of formation of the chromosome fusion nucleus, with its characteristic arrangement of three pairs of chromosome complexes, in the smooth type of bacterium, is obscure, and to refer the problem to the supposed precursor cells, with their three pairs of complexes, arranged in a more usual manner, does little to elucidate the problem. It is, however, almost certain that the trinucleate precursor cell does, in fact precede and not follow the fusion cell, because the latter appears invariably to undergo at least one nuclear division while the chromosome complexes are still packed closely together. The entire mechanism may be equivalent to the formation and dispersal of a symplasm, with the exchange of nuclear material ; a method of reproduction which is common in both fungi and protozoa. The symplasm is represented by the filamentous cell, which although far from formless, is an aggregate containing the nuclear material of several cells, into which it subsequently divides. The bacterial cell has so marked a tendency to adopt a filamentous form of growth that a comparatively disorganised filament of this kind may reasonably be compared to a symplasm in cells of less regular outline.

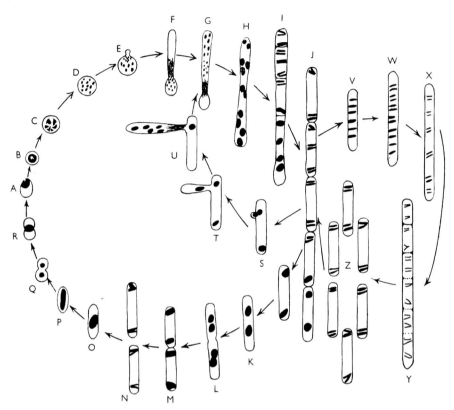

(Reproduced from the Journal of Hygiene).

FIG. **43**

THE LIFE-CYCLE OF *NOCARDIA*

A.   Microcyst.

B-G.   Germination.

G-J and *V-Z.*   Simple and complex fission.

S-U.   Branching.

K-N.   Simple fission in later vegetative stages.

O-A.   Maturation of the microcyst.

In most respects *Nocardia* behaves in a similar manner to the eubacteria and myxo-bacteria, but branching and germination by germ tube are typical of higher bacteria. (According to Morris).

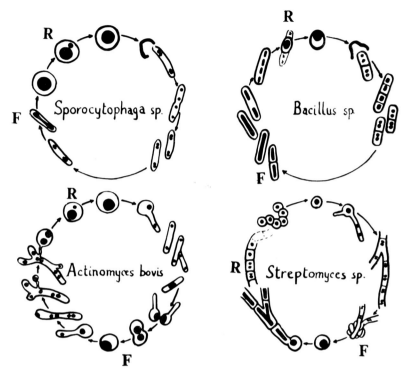

(Reproduced from Cold Spring Harbor Symposia).

FIG. 44

NUCLEAR CYCLES IN A VARIETY OF BACTERIA

F-fusion and R-reduction, in each case.   In *Sporocytophaga* and in non-sporing eubacteria there is no diploid generation.   In *Bacillus* there is a brief diploid (or polyploid) generation. In the higher forms, a secondary, diploid mycelium.

D: MICROCYST FORMATION IN MYXOBACTERIA AND EUBACTERIA

(2, 4, 5, 8, 10, 14, 16, 18, 19, 20, 24, 25, 26, 27)

A more obvious sexual process accompanies the formation of the resting nucleus, in these bacteria as in most others.   The resting nucleus is contained in a microcyst which may be larger or smaller than the vegetative bacterium. In eubacteria it is usually small, oval or spherical.   In some myxobacteria it is oblong, in others spherical.   In cytophagas, spherical and very large, compared with the vegetative cell.

The microcysts of some myxobacteria are contained in a complex fruiting body (Chapter VIII), but those of eubacteria and cytophagas are free.

The cytological processes accompanying the maturation of the microcyst are similar in all these cases. The nuclear material forms a chromatinic rod, similar to that which precedes sporulation in *Bacillaceæ*. The rod divides into

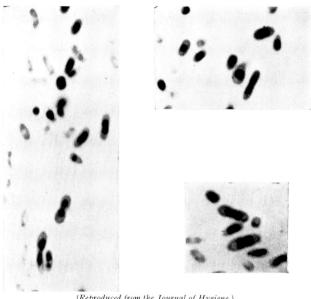

(Reproduced from the Journal of Hygiene.)

Fig. 45

MATURATION OF THE MICROCYST IN *BACT. COLI*

Sexual forms. The nuclear material may be seen at various stages of division and refusion. The division is usually incomplete and the fusion, autogamous. Occasionally it is complete and the fusion, truly sexual.

two spherical, nuclear bodies which again fuse and form the mature, resting nucleus. The process is almost identical in myxobacteria and most smooth eubacteria, in *Nocardia* and to some extent in the giant bacterium *Oscillospira*. Rough eubacteria usually form the resting nucleus from the secondary nuclear phase (Section *E*).

Two processes of fusion are discernible in the case of the myxobacteria and smooth eubacteria. Firstly, the rod-shaped nucleus arises by the fusion of the nuclear units of the cell, this divides and again fuses. The division of

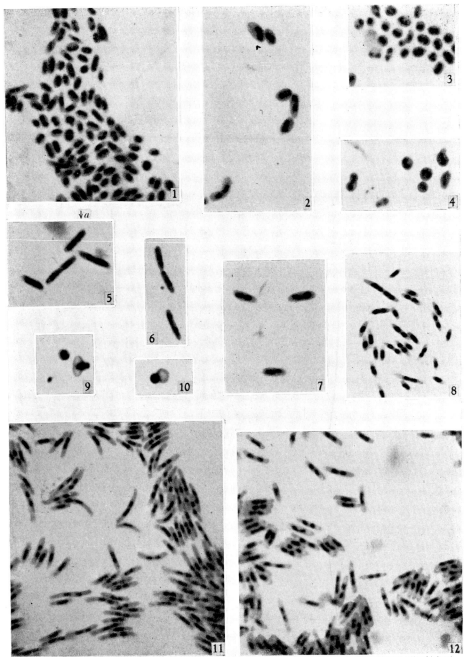

↓*a*

FIG 46

(See Legend on page 109)

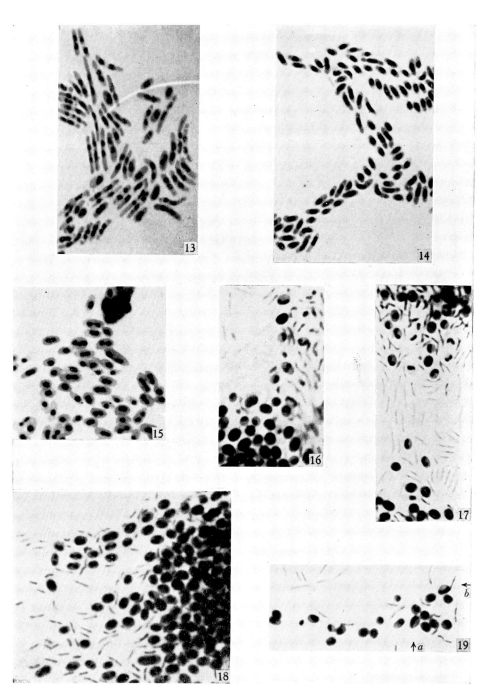

(*Photomicrographs by Dr. E. Klieneberger-Nobel. Reproduced from the Journal of General Microbiology*).

Fɪɢ 47

the nucleus may or may not be accompanied by complete division of the cell. If the gametic nuclei fuse within the original cell, then the process is autogamous, if the two gametes separate entirely and conjugate with other partners, the process is sexual. Cytological and genetical evidence agree that the former is most common but that the latter may occur upon occasion.

In eubacteria and cytophagas the division and refusion of the nucleus occurs in an elongated cell, often with a marked, central constriction, but in most myxobacteria the cell is already spherical.

A reduction process almost identical with that found in sporing genera occurs in myxobacteria, cytophagas, non-sporing eubacteria and *Nocardia*, as well as in *Actinomyces* (Section G below). The nucleus divides into two unequal parts and the smaller of these is eliminated. As in the case of sporers, sometimes more than one " polar body " is eliminated.

E: SEXUAL FUSION IN THE SECONDARY NUCLEAR PHASE

(8, 11, 23, 26, 27, 28)

One of the first records of sexual fusion in a non-sporing bacterium was made upon an organism in the secondary nuclear phase by Stoughton (1929, 1932). The condition is quite frequently adopted, in the latter stages of vegetative growth, especially by bacteria of rough morphology (Chapter IV). The bacterium contains a single, central, nuclear unit, probably a pair of chromosome complexes, and may often produce the appearance of end-to-end

---

FIGS. 46 AND 47 (*See* pp. 107 and 108)

THE CYTOLOGY OF MYXOBACTERIA

(1), (3), (4) *Myxococcus fulvus*, germinating microcysts, Giemsa × 3000.
(2) *Chondrococcus exiguus* (as above).
(5), (6) (8). *M. fulvus*, young vegetative cells, showing chromosomes, Giemsa × 3000.
(7) *Ch. exiguus* (as 5).
(9), (10) *M. fulvus*, burst microcysts, Giemsa × 3000.
(11) *M. virescens*, maturing culture, bacilli gathering to form microcysts, Giemsa × 3000.
(12) *M. fulvus*, maturing culture, Giemsa × 3000.
(13), (14), (15) *M. fulvus*, nuclear fusion, Giemsa × 3000.
(16), (17), (18), (19) *M. fulvus*, microcyst formation, Giemsa × 3000.

conjugations, with the nuclear material fused at the point of contact. Usually only a single pair of bacteria will conjugate thus, but there seems little reason to doubt that the star-like clusters which have been reported in *Phytomonas tumefaciens* and in cytophagas, as well as in many other genera, are exactly similar, multiple conjugations. In the case of *Ph. tumefaciens* the concentration of Feulgen-positive material at the centre of the cluster has been described.

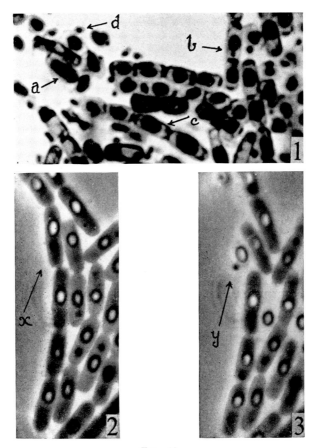

FIG. 48

THE NUCLEAR REDUCTION PROCESS

(1) In *Rhizobium* ; *a, b, c, d* represent stages in the maturation of the resting nucleus, and the elimination of a small daughter nucleus. (*Reproduced from Cold Spring Harbor Symposia*).

(2, 3) The elimination of the rejected daughter nucleus in *Bacillus* ; *x, y* shows two successive stages in the same organism. Phase-contrast photographs in the living state. (*Reproduced from Experimenta ,Cell Research, by permission of Prof. R. J. V. Pulvertaft*).

The resting nucleus may be formed directly from the secondary nucleus, with or without the intervention of a sexual process. In the case of *Bact. malvacearum*, described by Stoughton, the microcyst is extruded from the point of contact of the conjugating cells, or from the side of the bacterium when conjugation is not apparent. As the microcyst grows the mother cells shrink, and eventually disappear. This lateral extrusion of the microcyst has been reported in *Bacteriaceæ* by Mellon (1925), but the cytological processes

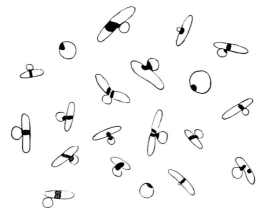

(After Stoughton. Reproduced from the Proceedings of the Royal Society.)

FIG. 49

MATURATION OF THE RESTING CELL IN *BACT. MALVACEARUM*

The microcyst is formed from the secondary nuclear phase, and is extruded laterally from the mother cell.

which accompanied it were not described. It is apparently no more than a variant of the commoner process of direct transformation of the vegetative cell.

F: SEXUALITY IN MYCOBACTERIA

(21, 22, 24, 25)

Among the many accounts of morphological development cycles in *M. tuberculosis*, only that of Lindegren and Mellon (1932, 1933) gives a convincing description of the accompanying cytological phenomena. It is interesting to observe, however, that it includes a sexual process, in the formation of the resting nucleus, which accords very closely with those which have already been described in other bacterial groups.

The process of formation of the resting nucleus commences by the con-jugation of two of the small cells produced by the fragmentation of the vegetative bacillus. Their small, spherical nuclei fuse, giving rise to a typical, eccentrically-staining, vesicular, resting nucleus.

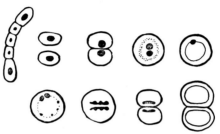

(*Modified after Lindegren and Mellon.*)

FIG. 50

MATURATION OF THE RESTING CELL IN *M. TUBERCULOSIS*

Upper line.—Sexual conjugation of cells derived from the bacillary form ; formation of the vesicular nucleus.
Lower line.—Reduction division. Two large chromosomes are formed from the vesicular nucleus and one passes to each daughter cell. The vesicular nucleus is reconstituted in each ; lacking the typical eccentric granule.

Reduction follows conjugation, as in all other cases where it has been described in bacteria, and resembles a meiotic cell division. The resting nucleus develops a number of granular threads, which contract, forming two chromosomes. The cell divides, and one chromosome passes to each daughter cell.

Beyond this stage the process ceases to resemble that which is found in eubacteria. The mature cell germinates by fission, into tetrads, and thus the small, elementary cells of the vegetative culture are restored (Chapter V).

This isolated description gains greatly in force by its remarkably close resemblance to the condition in most other groups, in the maturation of the resting nucleus, and especially to the more recent descriptions by Morris of the processes of initiation and maturation of the secondary phase in *Actinomyces bovis* (Section G below).

G: SEXUALITY IN STREPTOMYCES AND ACTINOMYCES

(17, 24, 27)

The descriptions of these genera are taken almost exclusively from the admirable descriptions of Klieneberger-Nobel (1947a) and Morris (1951a) respectively.

The nuclear material in the primary mycelium of streptomyces is in a form which resembles the chromosome complexes of young cultures of eubacteria. The secondary mycelium, from which the spores arise, contains rod-shaped, fusion nuclei. The sexual process which brings about this transformation is unlike any of those which have so far been described, in that a special, sexual organ is produced for the purpose. Branches arise from the primary mycelium, which may be much ramified or tightly curled at the ends. These become entangled with other, similar branches, forming " nests " of filamentous cells, within which the initial cells of the secondary mycelium arise. The initial cells are spherical or oval and contain a central nucleus. They germinate to form the secondary mycelium, with its rod-shaped fusion nuclei.

Spores are formed by the fragmentation of the fusion nuclei within special, aerial hyphæ arising from the secondary mycelium. The chromatinic material at first forms paired chromosomes which are transformed into the simple spherical spore nuclei.

The primary mycelium, which arises from the germination of the spores, is apparently haploid, like the spores themselves, and the secondary mycelium, diploid, but the details of the intervening sexual process, which presumably occurs in the mycelial " nests," are not described.

The nuclear material of the primary mycelium of the anaerobic actinomyces is also similar to that of vegetative eubacteria, but in this case the branching of the filaments is impermanent, and the mycelium less complex than in the streptomyces. The initial cells of the secondary phase arise by the conjugation of bacillary units from the primary mycelium, and germinate to produce an apparently diploid mycelium, which is branched but non-septate and coenocytic. The spores arise singly on short branches, and the reduction process which

H

precedes their maturation is similar to that already described for eubacteria (Sections *B, D* above).   A nuclear division gives one large and one small daughter nucleus, of which the latter is eliminated.

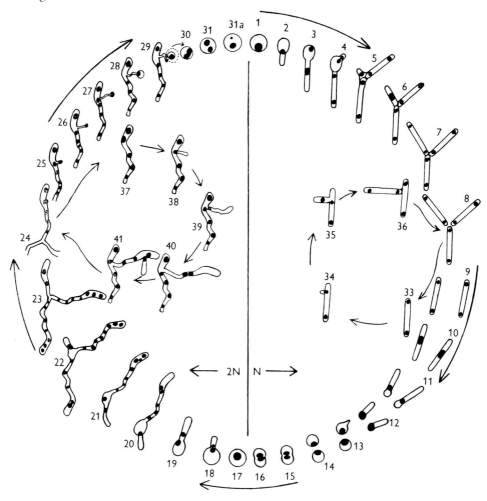

FIG. 51

THE LIFE-CYCLE OF ACTINOMYCES BOVIS

(1) Spore.
(2-4) Germination.
(5-8 and 33-36) Vegetative reproduction in the primary mycelium.
(9-17) Formation of " initial cell " by fusion of units from primary mycelium.
(18-21) Germination of " initial cell " to give coenocytic secondary mycelium.
(22-24 and 37-41) Growth and branching.
(25-31) Development and maturation of spore, nuclear reduction. (According to Morris).

H: SEXUAL FUSION IN PROTEUS AND
STREPTOBACILLUS

(13)

It has been stated that *Streptobacillus moniliformis* is capable of reproduction by the formation of spore-like bodies arising from swollen sporangia upon the filaments of the bacteria. These bodies are claimed to be sexual in origin, forming in other bacteria, including *Proteus*, at the edges of swarms where these make contact with other, similar swarms.

This interpretation will be discussed in Chapter VII.

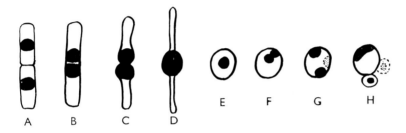

FIG. 52

Formation and maturation of the resting stage in the anaerobic actinomycete *Spherophorus*, according to Prévot. The resemblance between this process and that described independently for *Actinomyces bovis* is most striking (compare Fig. 51).

I: SUMMARY

A well-marked process of autogamous or sexual fusion accompanies the the formation of the resting nucleus in all groups of bacteria.

In sporing bacilli and streptomyces a longitudinal, rod-shaped fusion nucleus is formed, and from it haploid spores arise. In the case of the sporing bacilli the reduction process is very obvious, and precedes spore maturation.

In myxobacteria and non-sporing eubacteria the nucleus divides and reconjugates. The two gametes contain spherical, central nuclei, and fuse to form a microcyst containing a vesicular, resting nucleus. The vegetative bacterium is haploid and the reduction process precedes the maturation of the microcyst. A similar process has been recorded in the anaerobic actinomyces, and a reduction division occurs during maturation.

Sexual fusion may also occur in the secondary nuclear phase in eubacteria, and has been reported to take place at the edges of *Proteus* swarms.

Cytological evidence of the nuclear cycle indicates that the vegetative form is haploid, and that fusion is immediately followed at a varying interval of time by a reduction process with the elimination of one or more daughter nuclei. The gametes are homothallic. Fusion is occasionally sexual but more frequently autogamous. These conclusions are confirmed by genetical evidence.

The complex method of vegetative reproduction is also probably sexual. It is analogous to the formation and fragmentation of a symplasm.

BIBLIOGRAPHY

(1) ALLEN, L. A., APPLEBY, J. C. and WOLF, J. (1939) Zbl. f. Bakt. II. 100. 3.

(2) BADIAN, J. (1930) Act. Soc. Bot. Pol. 7, 55.

(3) BADIAN, J. (1933a) Arch. f. Mikrobiol. 4. 409.

(4) BADIAN, J. (1933b) Act. Soc. Bot. Pol. 10. 361.

(5) BEEBE, J. M. (1941) J. Bact. 42. 193.

(6) BISSET, K. A. (1948a) J. Gen. Microbiol. 2. 248.

(7) BISSET, K. A. (1948b) J. Hyg., Camb. 46. 173.

(8) BISSET, K. A. (1949) ibid. 47. 182.

(9) BISSET, K. A. (1951) Cold Spring Harbor Symposia. 16. 373.

(10) BISSET, K. A., Grace, J. B. and Morris, E. O. (1951) Exp. Cell. Res. 3. 388.

(11) BRAUN, A. C. and ELROD, R. P. (1946) J. Bact. 52. 695.

(12) DIENES, L. (1946) Cold Spring Harbor Symposia. 11. 51.

(13) FLEWETT, T. H. (1948) J. Gen. Microbiol. 2. 325.

(14) GRACE, J. B. (1951) J. Gen. Microbiol. 5. 519.

(15) KLIENEBERGER-NOBEL, E. (1945) J. Hyg., Camb. 44. 99.

(16) KLIENEBERGER-NOBEL, E. (1947a) J. Gen. Microbiol. 1. 33.

(17) KLIENEBERGER-NOBEL, E. (1947b) ibid. 1. 22.

(18) KRZEMIENIEWSKA, H. (1930) Act. Soc. Bot. Pol. 7. 507.

(19) KRZEMIENIEWSKI, H. and S. (1928) ibid. 5. 46.

(20) LEDERBERG, J. (1948) Heredity. 2. 145.

(21) LINDEGREN, C. C. and MELLON, R. R. (1932) J. Bact. 25. 47.

(22) LINDEGREN, C. C. and MELLON, R. R. (1933) Proc. Soc. Exp. Biol. Med. 30. 110.

(23) MELLON, R. R. (1925) J. Bact. 10. 579.

(24) MORRIS, E. O. (1951a) J. Hyg., Camb. 49. 46.

(25) MORRIS, E. O. (1951b) ibid. 49, 175.

(26) PULVERTAFT, R. J. Y. (1950) J. Gen. Microbiol. 4. xiv.

(27) PRÉVOT, A. R. (1953) Symp. *Actino*. Rome. vi. Int. Cong. Microbiol.

(28) SCHAUDINN, F. (1902) Arch. Protistenk. 1. 306.

(29) SCHAUDINN, F. (1903) ibid. 2. 421.

(30) STANIER, R. Y. (1942) Bact. Rev. 6. 143.

(31) STOUGHTON, R. H. (1929) Proc. Roy. Soc. B. 105. 469.

(32) STOUGHTON, R. H. (1932) ibid. 111. 46.

(33) TUFFERY, A. A. (1954) J. Gen. Microbiol. 10. 342.

CHAPTER VII

Life-Cycles in Bacteria

A. GENERAL

THE life-cycles of many bacteria are simple and direct. A cell in the resting stage is transplanted upon a new source of food. It germinates into the vegetative form and multiplies by simple, asexual fission, as well as by more complex methods (Chapter V). The nucleus of the vegetative cell may adopt a variety of appearances. Often it is semi-permanently in the active condition, without a nuclear membrane, and with the chromatinic material in the form of chromosomes or chromosome complexes (Chapter IV).

When the food supply begins to be exhausted, and when the waste-products of the culture have accumulated to such an extent as to interfere with metabolic activity, a new generation of resting forms is produced, by a sexual process (Chapter VI). The resting cells may be contained in elaborate fruiting bodies, or may be free. They may or may not be especially resistant. The nucleus is central and vesicular, often staining with an eccentric, chromatinic granule (Chapter IV).

In almost every case the diploid phase is short, fusion being almost immediately followed by a reduction division (Chapters VI and X).

B: THE LIFE-CYCLE IN MYXOBACTERIA
(2, 3, 16, 29, 34, 35)

The type of life-cycle described in the previous section is found in its most advanced form in myxobacteria.

The unit is the swarm. When a ripe fruiting body, usually windborne, falls upon a suitable substrate, it releases the thousands of microcysts which it contains, and each of these germinates to form a vegetative bacterium, the whole constituting the swarm.

The swarm moves out over the substrate, feeding and multiplying as it goes. From time to time fruiting bodies are produced, under the influence of a specific factor elaborated by the vegetative cells. These are formed by the aggregation of vegetative bacteria, some of which are transformed into microcysts, and some of which are sacrificed to assist in the formation of the stalk and wall of the fruiting body. The mature fruiting body, in some genera, is of great complexity, and may be borne upon a long stalk, in others it is sessile and simple in form. When ripe, the fruiting body is released from its stem and blows away in the wind. If it alights upon a suitable substrate it germinates and releases the swarm to repeat the cycle.

This type of multicellularity is not peculiar to myxobacteria. It occurs also in an interesting group of organisms, the *Acrasieæ*. In this case the unit of the swarm is an amoeboid cell instead of a bacterium, but the cycle is in every other way similar. Myxobacteria and *Acrasieæ* are probably not in any way related, but have merely adopted a similar mode of life. They also resemble one another in being predatory upon saprophytic bacteria, in the soil, although pathogenic myxobacteria do exist.

C: THE LIFE-CYCLE IN EUBACTERIA
(1, 4, 5, 7, 28, 37, 38)

The condition in eubacteria and myxobacteria is not dissimilar, although superficially it may appear to be so. Bacteriologists working with pure cultures upon otherwise sterile media may derive a false impression of the extent to which the distribution of bacteria is achieved by single cells, whether spores or otherwise, inaugurating new growth. Such conditions do not obtain in nature. The soil, which is the natural habitat of most bacteria, swarms with micro-organisms of every kind, and competition must often

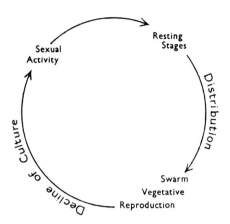

THE LIFE-CYCLE IN EUBACTERIA AND MYXOBACTERIA

be too keen to permit of the immediate success of a single transplant, of this kind. New substrates are more frequently introduced to micro-organisms already present, than *vice versa*, and are thus inoculated with a considerable number of spores or resting cells, derived from the last period of growth in the same area.

In effect, therefore, the unit of growth and reproduction, in eubacteria as in myxobacteria, is the swarm or bacterial culture. The culture grows and ages, physically and physiologically, exactly like a multicellular organism, and differs from one mainly in the lack of specialisation of its component cells. In myxobacteria some degree of specialisation has been achieved in the formation of the various parts of the fruiting body, but in eubacteria all cells have an equal reproductive potential.

The similarity between the cytology of the reproductive processes of the two groups makes it apparent that their life-cycles are basically alike, and this similarity is increased by the existence of the cytophagas which appear to be intermediate between them in many respects ; resembling eubacteria in their saprophytic habit and absence of fruiting bodies, myxobacteria in the large microcyst and the morphology of the bacterium.

What is known of the cycle in *Mycobacterium* and *Nocardia* is entirely comparable in most respects (Chapters V and VI), but these organisms have some characters in common with the higher bacteria, to which they are probably related.

D: THE LIFE-CYCLE IN HIGHER BACTERIA

(32, 37)

In streptomyces a truly multicellular organism is formed, and thus the problem of distribution entails the liberation of free, reproductive units, small airborne spores. Streptomyces resemble moulds in their general form, and this resemblance extends to their mode of reproduction.

The spore alights upon a suitable substrate, and germinates to form the primary mycelium. Sexual branches arise upon the primary mycelium and initiate the aerial hyphæ which bear the spores.

During its lifetime the organism or colony produces spores continuously, while conditions are suitable. In eubacteria, upon the other hand, the reproductive cells arise only in an ageing culture, when almost all may be thus transformed.

The true *Actinomyces bovis*, which is a parasite and microaerophilic also has a complete life-cycle with a primary and secondary mycelium. But the spores, which cannot be expected to benefit by aerial distribution, are borne singly and in relatively small numbers. This may represent a degenerate condition.

E: THE LIFE-CYCLE IN CHLAMYDOBACTERIA AND CAULOBACTERIA

(15, 20, 21, 28)

In chlamydobacteria, such as the filamentous, iron bacterium *Sphaerotilus discophorus*, as in the case of streptomyces, the organism is essentially sessile and multicellular, so that it must be provided with a distributive mechanism

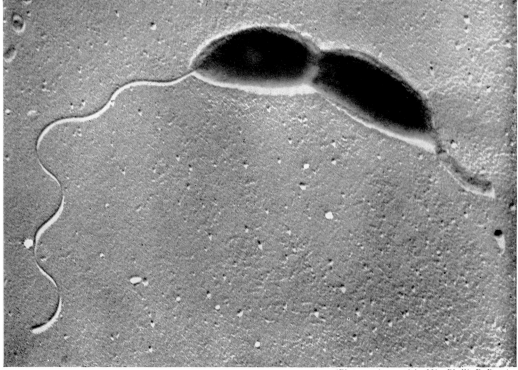

(*Electron micrograph by Miss Phyllis E. Pease*).

FIGS. 53 AND 54

THE LIFE-CYCLE OF *CAULOBACTER*

The life-cycle of the true, stalked caulobacteria provides an example of the alternation of sessile and motile generations, such as is commonly found in other biological groups. In Fig. 53 the entire cycle is seen foreshortened. The stalked cell is producing a flagellate daughter cell. Fig. 54 shows the complete life-cycle. The stalked generation (1) is shown in process of division. In (2) the flagellate daughter cell is shown. In (3) are two flagellate cells in the process of becoming sessile. In the upper example the stalk has already developed, but the flagellum (slightly outlined for clarity) is retained. In the lower example the stalk is in an early stage of development. Electron micrographs, gold-shadowed. Fig. 53 and Fig. 54 (1) × 20,000; Fig. 54 (2), (3) × 15,000.

for reproductive purposes. Chlamydobacteria are aquatic and instead of aerial spores produce motile swarmer cells, which swim actively by means of flagella.

The vegetative cells grow as a long filament, surrounded by a sheath of colloidal iron. At the ends of the sheath the cells may be transformed into flagellated swarmers, which swim off to found new filamentous colonies.

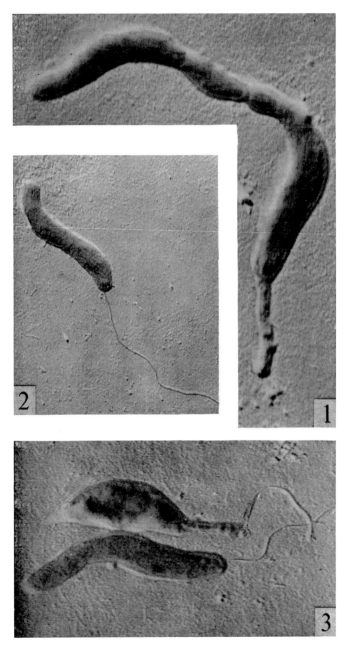

FIG 54

(*See Legend on page* 122)

It is unfortunate that the cytology of this interesting process has never been properly described. The vegetative cells are quite similar to those of eubacteria, but the minute structure of the swarmers has never been described.

Certain caulobacteria possess a short cycle which is rather similar. The sessile, stalked bacterium produces a succession of motile, flagellated daughter cells, which swim actively until they find a suitable attachment upon which to form a stalk, and produce a new, sessile generation.

There is no apparent difference between the daughter cell which, having the terminal stalk, remains attached to the substrate, and that which, being free, swims away, but the effect is exactly as though a sessile, asexual generation were producing a series of motile buds. If this type of organism possesses a sexual stage, it is in the motile cells that it must be sought.

F: GONIDIA AS A STAGE IN THE BACTERIAL LIFE-CYCLE

(1, 6, 7, 17, 18, 22, 36, 40, 42, 43)

This question, so far as it relates to the tubercle bacillus, has already been discussed (Chapter V). Of the many claims that bacteria of other groups may reproduce by the liberation of tiny, filterable granules or gonidia, few have been accompanied by sufficiently detailed, cytological information.

By far the most perfect examples of gonidial reproduction are provided by the nitrogen-fixing bacteria *Azotobacter* and *Rhizobium*. The details in both cases have long been known, but have been described in a rather unconvincing manner, and, in the case of *Rhizobium*, not entirely accurately. It was supposed that large " barred " bacilli fragmented to form small coccoid swarmers ; each dark bar representing the genesis of a single swarmer. In fact, the process is alike in both genera. The tiny, polar-flagellated gonidia form within the lumen of large mother cells, and are released by rupture of the cell wall. The mother cells in the case of *Rhizobium* are divided by basophilic septa, probably secretory in function, and these septa are the " bars " of the earlier account.

A second, larger type of gonidium, resembling a small vegetative cell, may be produced by *Azotobacter*.

Many accounts of gonidial reproduction refer to spore-bearing bacilli, and of these the paper published by Allen *et al.* (1939) is the most detailed and convincing. These workers described the occurrence of small, refractile granules in the cytoplasm of the bacillus. These granules appeared to reproduce by fission, and were liberated from the cell and transformed into small rods which grew up into normal bacilli. The granules were capable of passing through a Berkefeld filter.

The process is probably typical of many which have been described, rather less convincingly, by other authors. It is possible that the G forms of Hadley (1927 *et seq.*), which have been reported as tiny cells, forming correspondingly tiny colonies among the normal colonies of several different bacterial species, may be of a similar nature, but in this case also, the evidence is more voluminous than enlightening.

The existence of a granular reproductive phase in spirochætes has long been a subject of controversy. Recent studies have confirmed, however, that members of this group may reproduce both by transverse fission and by the formation of large cysts, usually at the end, but occasionally in the middle of the organism. These cysts contain several small spirochætes, sometimes in a granular form. In the experience of the author the cysts stain more deeply than the vegetative spirochætes with basic dyes, and thus probably have an increased nucleic acid content.

There is evidence that the granules or gonidia are more resistant than the vegetative spirochætes, and the latter may survive adverse conditions in this form.

The details of the processes of formation and germination have not been described, nor is it known whether a sexual process is involved.

G: L-ORGANISMS

(8, 9, 10, 11, 12, 13, 14, 23, 24, 25, 26, 27, 30, 31, 33, 39, 41)

In several papers, Klieneberger (1935 *et seq.*) described the occurrence, in cultures of *Streptobacillus moniliformis*, of small colonies resembling those of the organism of bovine pleuropneumonia. She considered these colonies,

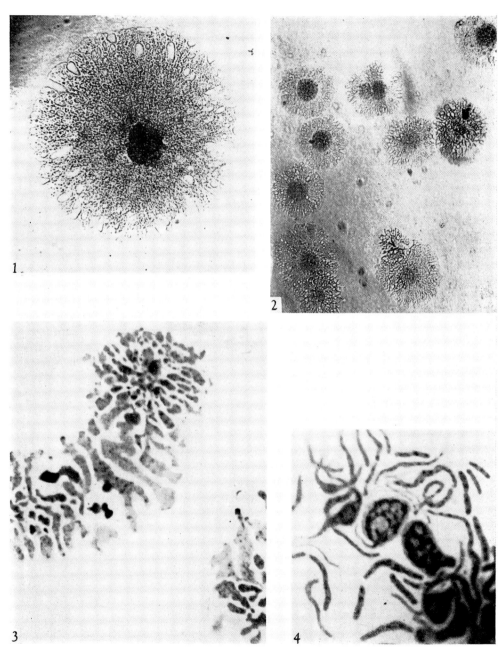

(Photomicrographs by Dr. E. Klieneberger-Nobel.   Reproduced from the Journal of Hygiene).

FIG 55

and the occasional swelling of the bacterial filaments which accompanied their presence, to be evidence of a parasitic or symbiotic condition between the L-organism, as it was termed, and the bacterium. Dienes (1939 *et seq.*), upon the other hand, believed the L-organism to be a gonidial stage in the life-cycle of the bacterium. He claimed that the minute colonies were liberated from the swellings upon the bacterial threads, and that the tiny, component organisms grew up into *Str. moniliformis.* Klieneberger stated that the L-organism could be subcultured upon artificial medium for several years, without reverting to a bacterial condition.

Dienes also claimed that the swollen cells, which liberated the L-gonidia, were the result of sexual fusions between filaments, and that similar swellings occurred at the point of contact of *Proteus* swarms (Chapter VI). Similar swollen filaments have been observed to occur in a variety of bacterial genera, and L-organisms have been found in cultures of *Neisseria gonorrhoeae* and *Fusiformis necrophorus.*

Studies with the electron microscope support the life-cycle hypothesis, and there is little doubt that the L-organisms are in fact a gonidial stage in the life-cycle of these bacteria. Klieneberger has herself adopted this view in a recent paper (1949), and claims that the reproductive bodies arise from a sexual process.

The main difference between this phenomenon and gonidial reproduction in many other bacterial groups (Section F, above) is the apparent capacity of the L-stage to reproduce itself for many generations without returning to the bacterial condition.

FIG. 55

THE L-STAGE IN THE BACTERIAL LIFE-CYCLE

(1), (2) Colonies of the L-form of *Fusiformis necrophorus* × 200. This gonidial stage reproduces for some time without reverting to the bacterial form.

(3) A colony of the L-form, fixed and stained, *in situ* × 2000.

(4) *Fusiformis necrophorus,* the bacterial form, showing reproductive swellings. Giemsa × 3500.

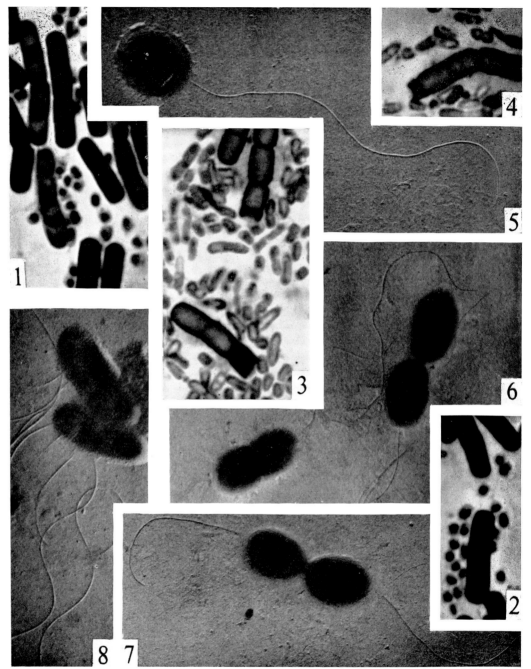

Fig 56

H: SUMMARY

The type of life-cycle which is seen in its most perfect form in myxobacteria is also common to most other bacterial groups.

The resting stage, a group of microcystic cells, is transplanted upon a fresh medium, and germinates to produce the vegetative culture or swarm, which is the reproductive condition. When the substrate is exhausted the vegetative cells undergo a sexual process to produce the resting stage, which remains in that condition until again transplanted, or until the food supi ly is renewed.

The resting stage may be a resistant spore, or may not be markedly resistant, except to inanition. In the case of myxobacteria the microcysts are contained in elaborate fruiting bodies.

Sessile bacteria, the mycelium-forming streptomyces, filamentous chlamy-dobacteria and stalked caulobacteria can only be distributed by the agency of free, reproductive units. Streptomyces produce aerial spores in large numbers, and the aquatic chlamydobacteria and caulobacteria produce motile swarm cells, which swim away and found new colonies.

Many bacteria may produce very small gonidia from which typical bacteria are regenerated, but little is known of their nature, or the circumstances under which they are formed. Such gonidia are found in their most perfect form in the life-cycles of *Rhizobium*, *Azotobacter* and certain spiral bacteria.

Fig. 56

BACTERIAL GONIDIA

The production of gonidia is seen in its most perfect form in the root-nodule symbiotic bacterium *Rhizobium*. Small, spherical gonidia are released by the rupture of the cell wall in specialised, large, septate mother-cells. The gonidia have single or occasionally double flagella and show appearances suggestive of conjugation. They rapidly grow up into small bacilli.

(1, 2) Production of gonidia. (Acid-Giemsa, × 3000).

(3, 4) The same. (Tannic-acid-violet).

(5) Electron micrograph of gonidium. (Gold-shadowed, × 20,000).

(6, 7) Electron micrographs of gonidia showing appearances suggestive of conjugation. It will be noticed that both members of a pair have well-developed flagella, which would not normally appear in cases of division, where one daughter cell would have short flagella or none. (× 16,000).

(8) Small, motile bacterium, replacing gonidia in some strains of *Rhizobium*. (× 16,000).

I

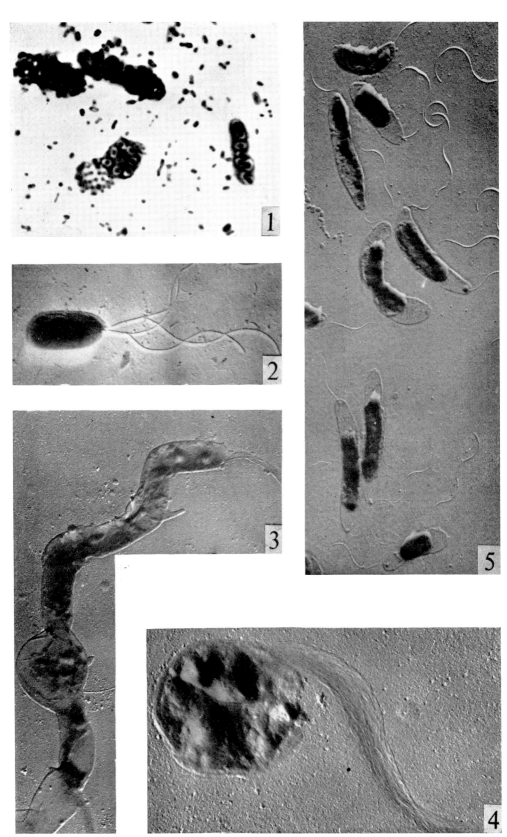

((1) and (2) reproduced from the Journal of General Microbiology; remainder by courtesy of Miss Phyllis Pease).

FIG 57

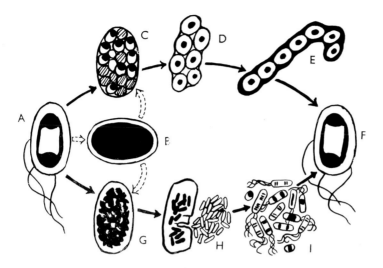

FIG. 58

LIFE-CYCLE OF AZOTOBACTER

An extraordinary degree of complexity is found in the life-cycle of the nitrogen-fixing bacterium *Azotobacter*. Not only does this organism produce spore-like cysts (not illustrated here), but two distinctly different types of gonidia.

The vegetative cell (*A*) becomes packed with tiny replicas of itself (*C*), or with motile gonidia (*G, H*). In both cases, the cycle is initiated by the production, within the mother-cell of an undifferentiated mass of Gram-positive material (*B*) ; traces of Gram-positivity may be retained to a later stage of gonidium production.

The large gonidia (*C, D, E*) grow up directly into typical vegetative cells, and are retained within the remains of the mother-cell wall. The small, motile gonidia (*G, H, I*) may reproduce for several generations as small, Gram-negative bacteria.

FIG. 57

BACTERIAL GONIDIA

Bacterial gonidia are also well seen in *Azotobacter*, which produces more than one kind, and in some spiral organisms.

(1) *Azotobacter* mother cells showing large and small gonidia (compare Fig. 58). The large types grow directly into vegetative cells, the small gonidia may reproduce as such for several generations. (Gram's stain, × 3000).

(2) Small gonidium of *Azotobacter*. It resembles those of *Rhizobium* but has more flagella and is less nearly spherical. (Electron micrograph, gold-shadowed, × 16,000).

(3) Electron micrograph of *Spirillum* sp. showing attached cysts, from which the gonidia are produced. (× 6000).

(4) Mature cyst with flagella still attached. (× 12,000).

(5) Developing gonidia, of *Spirillum*, each with a single polar flagellum. Note the blepharoplasts. (× 12,000).

BIBLIOGRAPHY

(1) ALLEN, L. A., APPLEBY, J. C. and WOLF, J. (1939) Zbl. f. Bakt. II. 100. 3.

(2) ANSCOMBE, F. J. and SINGH, B. N. (1948) Nature, Lond. 161. 140.

(3) BEEBE, J. M. (1941) J. Bact. 42. 193.

(4) BISSET, K. A. (1949) J. Hyg., Camb. 47. 182.

(5) BISSET, K. A. (1950) J. Gen. Microbiol. 4. 1.

(6) BISSET, K. A. and HALE, C. M. F. (1951) J. Gen. Microbiol. 5. 592.

(7) BISSET, K. A. and HALE, C. M. F. (1953) ibid. 8. 442.

(8) DIENES, L. (1939) J. Inf. Dis. 65. 24.

(9) DIENES, L. (1940) Proc. Soc. Exp. Biol. Med. 44. 470.

(10) DIENES, L. (1942) J. Bact. 44. 37.

(11) DIENES, L. (1943) Proc. Soc. Exp. Biol. Med. 53. 84.

(12) DIENES, L. (1946) Cold Spring Harbor Symposia. 11. 51.

(13) DIENES, L. (1947) J. Bact. 54. 231.

(14) DUGUID, J. P. (1948) J. Path. Bact. 60. 265.

(15) FISCHER, A. (1897) Vorlesungen uber Bakterien, Leipzig.

(16) GARNJOBST, L. (1945) J. Bact. 49. 113.

(17) HADLEY, P. (1927) J. Inf. Dis. 40. 1.

(18) HADLEY, P. (1937) ibid. 60. 129.

(19) HADLEY, P. (1939) ibid. 65. 267.

(20) HENRICI, A. T. and JOHNSON, D. E. (1935) J. Bact. 30. 61.

(21) HOUWINCK, A. L. (1949) Address to Soc. Gen. Microbiol.

(22) JONES, D. H. (1920) J. Bact. 5. 325.

(23) KLIENEBERGER, E. (1935) J. Path. Bact. 40. 93.

(24) KLIENEBERGER, E. (1936) ibid. 42. 587.

(25) KLIENEBERGER, E. (1938) J. Hyg., Camb. 38. 458.

(26) KLIENEBERGER, E. (1940) ibid. 40. 204.

(27) KLIENEBERGER, E. (1942) ibid. 42. 485.

(28) KLIENEBERGER-NOBEL, E. (1945) ibid. 44. 99.

(29) KLIENEBERGER-NOBEL, E. (1947a) J. Gen. Microbiol. 1. 33.

(30) KLIENEBERGER-NOBEL, E. (1947b) J. Hyg., Camb. 45. 407

(31) KLIENEBERGER-NOBEL, E. (1947c) ibid. 45. 410.

(32) KLIENEBERGER-NOBEL, E. (1947d) J. Gen. Microbiol. 1. 22.

(33) KLIENEBERGER-NOBEL, E. (1949) ibid. 3. 434.

(34) KRZEMIENIEWSKI, H. and S. (1926), Act. Soc. Bot. Pol. 4. 1.

(35) LEV, M. (1954) Nature, Lond. 173. 501.

(36) LOHNIS, F. (1921) Mem. Nat. Acad. Sci. 16. 1.

(37) MORRIS, E. O. (1951a) J. Hyg., Camb. 49. 46.

(38) MORRIS, E. O. (1951b) ibid. 49. 175.

(39) POKROWSKAJA, M. (1930) Zbl. f. Bakt. I. 119. 353.

(40) SHREWSBURY, J. F. D. and BARSON, G. J. (1949) The Life History of *Saprospira* Pers. Comm.

(41) SMITH, W. E., MUDD, S. and HILLIER, J. (1948) J. Bact. 56. 603.

(42) WORATZ, H. (1954) Zbl. f. Bakt. i. 160, 613.

(43) WYCKOFF, R. W. G., HAMPP, E. G. and SCOTT, D. B. (1948) J. Bact. 56. 755.

CHAPTER VIII

Macroformations

A: THE MYXOBACTERIAL FRUITING BODY
(11, 12, 14)

THE most perfect and elaborate multicellular structures formed by bacteria are the fruiting bodies of myxobacteria. Other macroscopic formations, however elaborate, are little but the result of the reaction between the growth potential of the organism and the physical restraint of the environment, and slight variations in the latter may affect the result to an apparently disproportionate extent. The fruiting body, however, although it may be prevented, by unsuitable conditions, from forming at all, is otherwise independent, in its form, of small environmental changes, and is characteristic of the species. The co-ordination of cellular activity which initiates the formation of the fruiting body is stimulated by a specific substance, analogous to a hormone which diffuses from the vegetative cells.

The great majority of these cells are transformed into typical microcysts and thus survive. Some are embodied in the stalk and envelope, and are sacrificed. Little is known of the mode of formation of these structures. It has been stated that the cells which take part in their formation are cemented together by dried mucus, but this appears to be mere supposition. It is known that the physical properties of the envelope vary considerably in different species, and it may even be entirely absent. The envelope varies especially in its physical strength and in its resistance to water. The fruiting bodies of some species of myxobacteria burst open as soon as they are wetted. Others remain intact. This characteristic has been considered to be of taxonomic value by some botanists, but there is no reason to believe that it indicates biological relationship. Whether the variation is due to differences in structure and composition of the envelope is not known.

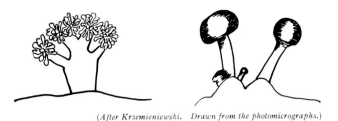

(After Krzemieniewski.   Drawn from the photomicrographs.)

Fig. 59

MYXOBACTERIAL FRUITING BODIES

B: THE MYXOBACTERIAL SWARM
(11, 12, 16)

In the vegetative stage also, myxobacteria give the impression of a degree of organisation far beyond that of other bacteria. The swarm moves outwards from the centre of germination in a regular fashion, following the lines of physical stress in the substrate. It concentrates in chosen areas, converging towards the incipient fruiting body, and piling up, the bacteria crawling over each other, to encyst in an elevated mass. The appearance of ordered purpose is most remarkable in so lowly an organism.

C: THE SWARM OF PROTEUS
(9, 12, 13, 15)

Some degree of cell-specialisation and organisation in the swarm of *Proteus* is indicated by Klieneberger-Nobel (1947) and other workers. It is suggested that the swarm commences its activity when an initial generation of large cells has produced a sufficient concentration of metabolites to provide the energy for swarming. The swarm cells are filamentous. They move out rapidly over the substrate until their reserve of energy is exhausted, and then rest until it becomes possible to repeat the process. Although this phenomenon is most advantageously seen upon the surface of an agar plate, there is no reason to believe that it does not occur in nature. *Proteus* may accordingly be regarded as having achieved a minor degree of cellular specialisation. It is also a temporary specialisation, because the swarm filaments, which are distributive in function, are the descendants as well as the parents of the " somatic " cells which accumulate the energy for the swarm. In multi-cellular animals and plants, although not always in fungi, the continuity of the germ plasm is very close, and the somatic cells proper have no reproductive function, when once the body of the organism is elaborated. Even in the case of myxobacteria, the microcysts may survive to germinate, but the cells which form the stalk and envelope of the fruiting body have no descendants.

D: CHLAMYDOBACTERIAL AGGREGATES
(5, 7)

As far as is known, the condition in chlamydobacteria, as typified by the filamentous, iron bacteria, resembles that in *Proteus*. The aggregates of gelatinous sheaths, the by-product of metabolism, are devoid of structural specialisation, except in so far as some are dead casts left behind by the cells which were responsible for their formation, whereas others are inhabited, and still increasing in size. The hold-fasts by which the ends of some types of filament are attached to the substrate are a possible exception to this rule. Those bacteria in which the character is most strongly developed are often classed as caulobacteria for precisely this reason.

After a period of vegetative growth, motile swarm cells are produced which swim away to form new colonies of filaments. There is no evidence that all the cells comprising the sessile filaments may not be equally capable of transformation into swarmers ; and indeed, what little is known of their cytology suggests a close resemblance to eubacteria, in this and other respects.

E: THE MEDUSA-HEAD COLONY
(1, 2, 3, 6)

In most bacteria the colony, however complex its structure, is an accidental growth, each cell of which is equivalent to all the others. The colony does not alternate with the swarm, but is itself the swarm, or vegetative mass. Where conditions are such that motile bacteria may exercise their motility, no colony is formed at any stage of culture. Colonies are not confined to conditions of artificial culture, although there they appear in their most perfect form.

The type of bacterial colony whose structure was first recognised, although not understood, was the so-called " medusa-head " colony of the anthrax bacillus. This form of colony, which consists of long, coiled, bacillary threads, is common to all bacteria of what we have termed rough morphology. In the case of the anthrax bacillus, and similar, large, spore-bearing bacilli, it is easily seen with a hand lens, whereas the much smaller size of, for instance, lactobacilli, renders it less obvious, so that its presence, except in these large genera, was long unsuspected.

Although it has long been known that the virulent anthrax bacillus possesses this type of colony, whereas the smooth colonies of the avirulent anthrax vaccine were composed of individual bacilli, the obvious corollary that the respectively virulent and avirulent smooth and rough colonies of *Bacteriaceæ* might possess the same type of structure in each case, escaped attention until much later. This was partly due to the studies which several different workers made upon the mode of cell division in smooth and rough strains of bacteria (Chapter V), which, by crediting rough bacteria with a " snapping " mode of division, erroneously claimed that the rough colony was composed of zig-zag chains of bacilli. This error, which has persisted for a quarter of a century, and is included in nearly all text-books of bacteriology, would never have arisen if these observations had been checked by examination of a rough colony, *in situ*, for it can readily be seen that the structure of a rough colony of a typhoid bacterium, and the " medusa-head " colony of the anthrax bacillus are identical.

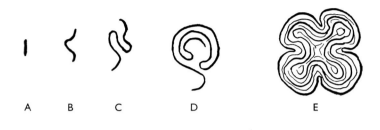

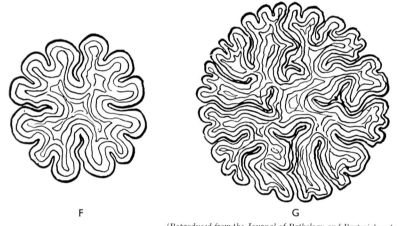

(Reproduced from the Journal of Pathology and Bacteriology.)

Fig. 60

STAGES IN THE GROWTH OF A MEDUSA-HEAD COLONY

A.   Original bacillus.

B, C.   Elongation and looping.

D.   Primary coil.

E.   Further growth, against the friction of the medium causes infolding of the coil.

F.   Secondary infolding of the coil.

G.   Continued growth of all parts of the colony causes complex folding and convolution.

The structural complexity, even beauty, of this type of colony has tended to produce the impression that there exists an intrinsic tendency towards the formation of the structure, as in the case of a true, multicellular organism. This is not so. A rough bacillus growing upon a frictionless surface, would produce a straight, or slightly spiral thread of indefinite length. Upon an agar plate, however, after the thread has grown a short way across the surface, its rigidity is not sufficiently great to permit it to extend further in a straight line. It therefore kinks, and because of its slightly spiral growth, tends to form flat coils upon the surface of the plate. All portions of this primary coil are growing simultaneously, and to accommodate this growth it produces

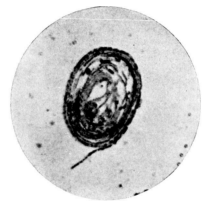

(*Reproduced from the Journal of Pathology and Bacteriology.*)

FIG. 61

GROWTH OF A ROUGH COLONY

Primary coil of a rough colony. *Shigella flexneri,* impression preparation × 700.

secondary loops and coils, and upon them still further and more complex convolutions. The outer portions of the colony lie flat upon the medium, and the internal coils overlie one another to a small extent.

The appearance and complexity of the colony vary with the rigidity of the bacterial thread, and the resistance of the surface of the medium. Colonies upon lactose-taurocholate agar may be noticeably flat and widespread, presumably in consequence of the high concentration of electrolytes and low surface-tension of such media.

Bacteria of rough morphology vary considerably in rigidity between such extremes as *Bacillus mycoides*, which is so rigid that it seldom produces any structure more complex than a primary coil, and grows out, as long threads across the agar, and, upon the other hand those rough *Bacteriaceæ* whose colonies are almost indistinguishable from smooth variants.

Rough colonies are not confined to the surface of artificial culture medium. They may form wherever a flat surface is presented to growth, provided that the substrate is not too fluid.

The structure of these colonies may be entirely disguised by the production of mucoid capsular material. The anthrax bacillus may produce its polypeptide capsule under suitable cultural conditions, of which CO_2 tension is one of the most important. The phenomenon of smooth→rough variation in pneumococci is entirely concerned with the production or loss of polysaccharide capsular material, concealing or revealing the rough appearance of the colony (Section G).

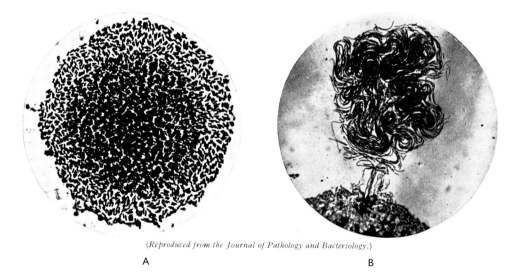

(*Reproduced from the Journal of Pathology and Bacteriology.*)

A   B

FIG. 62

SMOOTH AND ROUGH COLONIES

A. Smooth colony, *Bact. coli*, impression preparation × 500.
B. Rough colony arising from the perimeter of a smooth colony, *Shigella flexneri*, × 300.

F: SMOOTH COLONIES

(1, 2)

There is little to be said of the structure and mode of formation of the colonies of smooth bacterial variants. The constituent bacteria separate completely after cell division (Chapter III), and produce a structureless colony. It tends to be less flat than the medusa-head colony, because its edges lack the cohesion which is necessary to force their way out over the medium. Consequently it is a less efficient colony, because so great a proportion of the component cells lose contact with the substrate. Such colonies are often far from truly smooth in appearance, as surface concentrations of hydrophobe lipo-proteins or insoluble polysaccharides may give them a dusty or even a rocky appearance. Alternatively, like rough colonies, they may be enveloped in a mass of mucoid capsular material.

G: ROUGH AND SMOOTH COLONIES OF STREPTOCOCCI

(1, 2)

Streptococci and pneumococci, like rod-shaped bacteria, may grow in the form of threads and chains, or may separate completely after cell division. Accordingly, the former produce a modified medusa-head colony, and the latter a relatively structureless colony. The phenomenon of smooth→rough variation in the pneumococcus, as usually described, is not, however, concerned with this change, but with the loss of the capsule, which exposes the rough structure of the long-chained colony (Section E above). No distinction is drawn, by most bacteriologists, between S→R variation, as it is termed, in bacteria and in pneumococci. Both are associated with an antigenic change in the surface material, and both with an alteration in the appearance of the colony, as seen by the naked eye ; but the reason for this difference is not the same in each case, and the employment of the same expression to describe two phenomena which are analogous without being homologous, is unfortunate and has given rise to a certain amount of confusion.

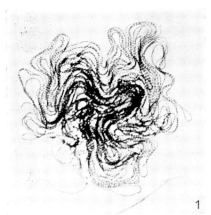
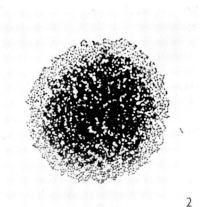

1   2

(Reproduced from the Journal of General Microbiology.)

FIG. 63

COLONIES OF STREPTOCOCCI

1.   Long-chained " rough " colony.
2.   Short-chained " smooth " colony.
     Impression preparations × 300.

H: COLONIES OF STREPTOMYCES

(4, 10)

The colonies of streptomyces may logically be considered as single, multi-cellular organisms, in which the functions of the various types of component cell are almost completely specialised.   The colony consists of a vegetative, haploid, primary mycelium, upon which arises a reproductive, diploid, secondary mycelium.   The condition is similar to that which obtains in higher fungi.   The spores are specialised distributive cells, and a single spore may give rise to the complete colony.   Although fragments of mycelium will grow if they are transplanted, the colony is essentially a unit which remains fixed upon its substrate, so long as the food supply permits, and it reproduces solely by the release of spores.   The cells of the mycelium perish when the food supply is exhausted or when conditions become unsuitable for growth.

Thus, in bacteria, the type of multicellularity represented by the swarm finds its greatest perfection in myxobacteria, the sessile colony in the strep-tomyces.   In each the mode of reproduction and distribution is admirably designed to the case.

I: COLONIES OF CAULOBACTERIA

(7, 8)

The aggregates formed by stalked caulobacteria may consist of small clumps attached to a single point upon the substrate, or of free colonies, in the form of rosettes or ribbons, composed of numerous bacteria joined together by their stalks.

 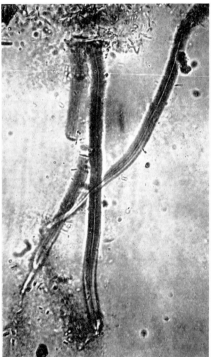

(Material kindly provided by Miss B. G. Fewins).

FIG 64   FIG 65

FIG. 64

CHLAMYDOBACTERIAL AGGREGATES

A group of filaments of the chlamydobacterium *Sphaerotilus discophorus*. The sheath is composed of colloidal ferric hydroxide. The older portions are the thickest and may be vacant. The growing filaments protrude from the sheath at the thinner end. (Unstained, × 1000).

FIG. 65

CAULOBACTERIAL AGGREGATES

A colony of *Caulobacter* attached to filaments of *Sphaerotilus*. Each cell has an independent very fine stalk. (Unstained, × 1500).

Cell-division is transverse, as in all other bacteria, although the stalk is attached to one end of the cell.   One daughter cell therefore remains attached, the other develops a flagellum and swims away until it encounters a suitable substrate, upon which it settles.   A stalk is developed and the flagellum degenerates.   This process is really a simple life-cycle with alternate sessile and free-living generations (Chapter VII).

J: SUMMARY

Bacteria may form multicellular structures of several different types. In some of these there is a certain degree of specialisation of function between the constituent bacteria, in others little or none.   In the myxobacterial fruiting body the majority of bacteria are transformed into reproductive microcysts, the minority become " somatic " cells in the stem or wall, and are sacrificed. This is also true, in a greater degree, of streptomyces.   The main body of the colony is sessile and vegetative, the spores alone are reproductive, and are borne upon a special, reproductive mycelium.   A similar specialisation of function divides the sessile and motile cells of chlamydobacteria and caulobacteria, and the swarming and non-swarming units of *Proteus*.

Streptomyces colonies are single units, arising from a single spore.   In eubacteria and myxobacteria the unit is the swarm or vegetative culture. The myxobacterial fruiting body is a device which ensures the distribution and survival of swarms, as such.   In the eubacteria distribution may be of single cells or of portions of swarms, usually the latter.   Eubacterial colonies have no intrinsic form, unlike fruiting bodies, their structure is due to the interaction of the forces of growth of the cells and mechanical resistance of the environment.   The swarm has little co-ordination except in myxobacteria and *Proteus*.

BIBLIOGRAPHY

(1) Bisset, K. A. (1938) J. Path. Bact. 47. 223.
(2) Bisset, K. A. (1939a) ibid. 48. 427.
(3) Bisset, K. A. (1939b) ibid. 49. 491.
(4) Erikson, D. (1947) J. Gen. Microbiol. 1. 45.
(5) Fischer, A. (1897) Vorlesungen uber Bakterien. Leipzig.

(6) FORSYTH, W. G. C. and WEBLEY, D. M. (1948) Proc. Soc. Appl. Bact. 34.

(7) HENRICI, A. T. and JOHNSON, D. E. (1935) J. Bact. 30. 61.

(8) HOUWINCK, A. L. (1949) Address to Soc. Gen. Microbiol.

(9) KLIENEBERGER-NOBEL, E. (1947a) J. Hyg., Camb. 45. 410.

(10) KLIENEBERGER-NOBEL, E. (1947b) J. Gen. Microbiol. 1. 22.

(11) KRZEMIENIEWSKI, H. and S. (1926) Act. Soc. Bot. Pol. 4. 1.

(12) KRZEMIENIEWSKI, H. and S. (1928) ibid. 5. 46.

(13) KVITTINGEN, J. (1939) Act. Path. Microbiol. Scand. 26. 24.

(14) LEV, M. (1954) Nature, Lond. 173. 501.

(15) LOMINSKI, I. and LENDRUM, A. C. (1947) J. Path. Bact. 59. 355.

(16) STANIER, R. Y. (1942) J. Bact. 44. 405.

K

CHAPTER IX

The Evolutionary Relationships of Bacteria

A: MORPHOLOGICAL EVIDENCE IN SYSTEMATICS

(3, 7, 8)

W HEREAS in other biological sciences the study of morphology and of systematics has, for the most part, been conducted by the same people, this is by no means true of bacteriology. Although acknowledging the importance of morphological studies, the systematists have, with a few, notable exceptions, rarely been engaged in them. Many have indeed failed to acquire sufficient familiarity with the subject to enable them fully to understand or evaluate cytological information where it is available.

On the other hand, many morphologists have been so closely engaged in the study of a single character, in a very small range of morphological types of bacteria, that they have been equally badly placed to attempt the formulation of a general scheme.

There is no doubt, however, that one of the most valuable contributions of the study of bacterial cytology to biological science is the information which it affords upon numerous, vexed problems of systematics. By its use an evolutionary system of classification, comparable with, and relatable to that employed in all other groups, may be applied to bacteria.

This system is the main subject of another book (*Bacteria*, 1952 ; published by E. & S. Livingstone Ltd.), but it is appropriate that its cytological aspects should be discussed here.

B: PREVIOUS SCHEMES OF CLASSIFICATION

(1, 4, 6, 8)

The best known classification of bacteria in current use is that of Bergey's Manual (6th Ed., 1948). The major defect of this system is that it is manifestly designed as a key, for identification purposes, rather than as a classification proper. Little or no attempt is made to relate the groups to one another, and some of these groups have been defined mainly upon physiological criteria and are decidely heterogeneous morphologically. Bacteria are accorded the status of a Class of Plants, the *Schizomycetes*, and are defined in a most un-satisfactory manner, by criteria which are either indifferent (*e.g.* they can be almost any shape), or negative, or demonstrably false, or both (*e.g.* they are supposed to be devoid of a " definitely organised nucleus "). The sole suggestion concerning the nature and relationships of bacteria is found in the words : " the closely related blue-green algae " ; and since the blue-green algae are the only major group in which flagella appear never to have existed, whereas they are found in plants, animals, fungi and bacteria, the closeness of this relationship is highly dubious. This misconception, which is of very long standing, is buttressed by the inclusion among the bacteria, as listed by Bergey's Manual, and especially among the autotrophic genera, of such obvious blue-green algae as *Beggiatoa*, (see Bisset & Grace, 1954, for further references).

The attempt of Kluyver and van Niel (1936) to introduce into bacterial systematics the element of evolutionary relationship which is the foundation of such systems in other sciences was an obvious reaction against the amorphous compilations which had previously been available. Their diagram of supposed evolutionary trends has proved exceedingly popular, and has frequently been reproduced. But, in the opinion of the present writer, certain defects, both in their argument and in their information, render their theories unacceptable.

The basic assumption of Kluyver and van Niel was that the coccal forms have the simplest morphology, and may thus be considered ancestral to all other bacteria. However, the evidence produced in the earlier chapters of this book indicates that the cocci are not a morphologically homogeneous group, and that most of them have a complex, septate structure, characteristic of the Gram-positive bacilli, to which they appear to be closely related. Of the Gram-negative cocci, some are degenerate, parasitic representatives of the Gram-positive genera, others may be derived independently from the

K 1

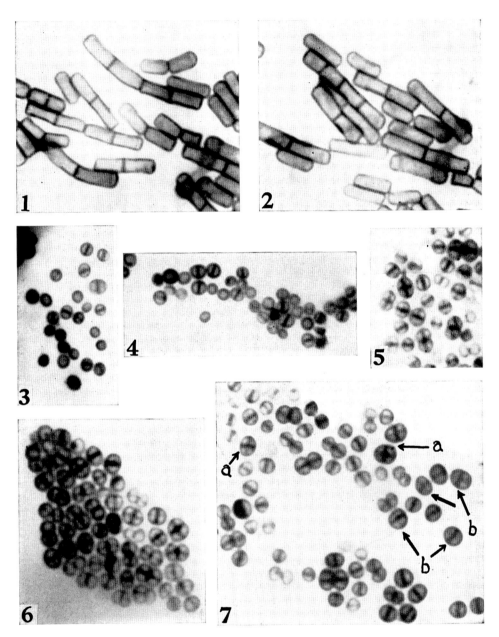

(*Reproduced from Experimental Cell Research*)

FIG. 66

Bacteriaceae, especially from the *Aerobacter* group (*c.f.* Bisset, 1952). It is, in addition, contrary to all experience in other natural groups to assume, even if the cocci were so simple in form as they appear to be, superficially, that they should, for that reason alone, be considered to be primitive. In almost all parallel cases, such apparently simple forms have proved to be descended from more complex creatures, and this is almost certainly true of the cocci.

The scheme of Kluyver and van Niel is open to criticism upon other grounds. It postulates four, divergent lines of evolution from the " ancestral " coccus ; the peritrichously flagellate rods, culminating in the sporing bacilli ; the cocci, culminating in sporing sarcinae (a group of very doubtful antecedents, since some at least are environmental variants of sporing bacilli) ; the polar flagellate rods leading to spirilla ; and fourthly, the progressively more branched forms, without flagella. This hypothesis postulates a multiple, independent origin for spores, flagella and the rod form, and even for Gram-positivity ; unless it is assumed that, having all these divergent potentialities in an immediately available genetic condition, this simple coccus was descended from a flagellated, rod-shaped, sporing ancestor. And this, although for entirely different reasons, I consider it probably was ! In its present form, however, the scheme is illogical and must be rejected. At the same time, it provides no clue to the relationships of bacteria with other groups, but appears to assume a separate origin from a tiny, spherical proto-cell, whereas their possession of flagella suggests a close relationship between bacteria and those flagellate protista which are the probable ancestors of all living cells, except blue-green algae. So far as the latter are concerned, no further comment is required upon the classical dictum that they share with the bacteria the lack of a true nucleus.

FIG. 66 (*See* p. 148)

RELATIONSHIP OF COCCI AND BACILLI

Preparations by Hale's method of the cell walls of *Bacillus*, compared with those of Gram-positive cocci. The former (1, 2) are symmetrically subdivided by cross-walls. The smaller cocci (3, 4) are normally divided by a single cross-wall ; the larger cocci (5, 6, 7) are also symmetrically subdivided into four or more cells, but each cross-wall is produced at right-angles to the preceding. *a*, complete subdivision ; *b*, an earlier stage of subdivision.

C: THE ANCESTRAL BACTERIUM
(2, 3, 4, 5, 7)

The preceding chapters have described the cytological characters of bacteria, but it is expedient, if it is wished to determine the nature of the ancestral bacterial type, to consider which of these characters are diagnostic of bacteria as a group.

The form of the vegetative nucleus, as a haploid, reductionally-dividing chromosome, lying at right-angles to the long axis of the cell, is such a character ; so also is the possession of monofibrillar flagella. In septate rods and filaments, the cells are separated by cross-walls which contain an element of true cell wall material. Leaving aside the question of the form of the nucleus, the two, latter characters serve quite conclusively to demarcate bacteria from blue-green algae, which have no flagella, and the filamentous forms of which are subdivided, not by true cross-walls but by relatively delicate septa.

The suggestion that the simpler bacteria may be derived by fragmentation from streptomyces-like forms of fungal origin is again unacceptable, since it suggests that flagella, lost for countless generations, might be regained. At the same time, while not entirely impossible, it is *a priori* improbable that an entire biological group, such as the bacteria, should have evolved from a complex terrestrial, to a simple aquatic form, whereas plants, animals and fungi alike seem to have done precisely the reverse.

If, on the other hand, it is considered more probable that the terrestrial bacteria are derived from the aquatic, it is obviously among the latter that the ancestral type must be sought. The most completely aquatic of all bacteria are the spirilla, and among these are to be found examples which appear to have several characters intermediate between typical bacteria and those small, saprophytic flagellates from which, in common with the fungi, it is reasonable to believe that they may have been derived.

The cell wall of these spirilla is less rigid, in some cases, than is that of other bacteria, but more so than that of the flagellates. And their polar flagella, although consisting of numerous separate fibrils, almost indistinguishable from typical, monofibrillar, bacterial flagella, beat as a single organ, and take their origin, not individually, but in tufts from single blepharoplasts.

In other respects the spirilla are admirably suited to the role of ancestral bacteria, since they may be Gram-positive or Gram-negative, septate or unicellular, and are capable of forming resting cells of various types, as well as of tiny, motile gonidia. But the most striking piece of evidence suggestive of a spirillar origin for bacteria is the observation of Pijper (1946) that many short rod-like bacilli are slightly spiral in morphology. The conclusions which Pijper drew from this observation, especially in respect of bacterial motility, have not been accepted by other workers in this field, but this tendency to a spiral form has proved to be general in almost all bacteria except cocci, and is of the utmost consequence in the present argument.

Thus, between the spirilla and the more specialised bacteria of every type there exists a complete series of morphological types, through which a line of descent may be traced. The main line appears to lead to an adaptation to a terrestrial environment, but specialised aquatic genera, such as caulobacteria and chlamydobacteria may also be brought into the scheme of reference and accorded their evolutionary position.

D: CHANGES IN FLAGELLAR PATTERN

(2, 3, 5, 6, 7)

The series of forms which connects *Spirillum* through *Vibrio* and *Pseudomonas* with *Bacterium*, by a gradual simplification of the elongate spiral into a short and only slightly spiral rod, and the change from polar, through lophotrichous to peritrichous flagellation, is reasonably obvious. But further progress among the more specialised *Bacteriaceae* leads on the one hand to *Proteus* with an enormous number of peritrichous flagella, and on the other to *Aerobacter* and related types which may have discarded their flagella altogether and adopted, in some cases, an almost coccal morphology. It is apparent that the latter have become completely adapted to a terrestrial existence, but the significance of peritrichous flagellation is obscure.

It is often assumed that the swarmers of *Proteus* are capable of exceptionally active motility in a fluid medium. In fact, when totally immersed they swim much less actively than *Vibrio* with its single, polar flagellum. The swarmers, with their thousands of flagella, are notable for their ability to move upon a

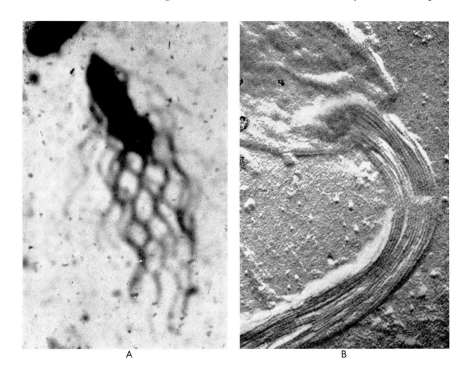

A   B

Fig. 67

THE EVOLUTION OF FLAGELLA

A. Typhoid bacterium showing typical peritrichous, monofibrillar flagella (silver impregnation).

B. Electron micrograph of complex flagellum of spirillum. (*By courtesy of Miss P. E. Pease*).

solid surface which is no more than moist. Under these conditions *Vibrio* is entirely immobilised unless the film of fluid is deep enough to permit it truly to swim. This observation, taken in conjunction with the evidence of habitat, leads inescapably to the conclusion that the profuse, peritrichous flagellation of *Proteus* and of certain sporing bacilli is an adaptation to life and motility, not in water, but in damp soil or decomposing organic matter.

The flagellation of typical *Bacteriaceae* represents an intermediate stage of evolution in this respect.

If any weight whatsoever can be placed upon the theory of recapitulation, the fact that the flagella in germinating microcysts of *Bacteriaceae* appear first in the polar position must be regarded as of some interest.

The problem of movement on land has been solved in a different manner by myxobacteria, which have adapted the cell wall to a crawling action, as in the Myxophyceae. The evidence at present available does not enable it to be determined whether this character is indicative of a relationship with the Myxophyceae or, through the more flexible spirilla and trichobacteria, with the typical bacteria, but cytological evidence is strongly in favour of the latter.

E: AERIAL DISTRIBUTION

(2, 3)

The most highly evolved bacteria appear to be those which have not only colonised the terrestrial habitat successfully, but have also developed adaptations for the aerial distribution of their reproductive elements. Of these the best example is provided by the streptomyces, which (presumably by evolutionary convergence) resemble minute moulds with aerial conidia, although their cytological structure and behaviour reveals their affinities with other bacteria. Here also, a complete series of forms of varying degrees of complexity serves to connect them, through *Nocardia* and *Mycobacteria*, with the Gram-positive eubacteria, among which other devices for aerial distribution may be found.

Consideration of this tendency provides a possible explanation of the nature of the bacterial endospore. Although less efficient in this respect than those of the streptomyces, the spores of Gram-positive bacilli are capable of being distributed in air and dust, and it is worthy of consideration whether it may be this factor, rather than their remarkable powers of resistance, which has conferred a genetical advantage upon their possessors.

Although the exact differences between the physico-chemical constitution of spores and vegetative cells of the same species remain obscure, it has repeatedly been claimed that the water-content of the former is reduced.

It is readily demonstrable that the spore-nucleus is in a condition of turgour, and these pieces of evidence, taken in conjunction with the exceedingly small relative size of most spores, and the resistance to denaturation of their proteins, suggest very strongly that the spore is reduced in size and weight by reduction of water-content, as an adaptation to aerial distribution, and that its resistance to heat and antiseptics follows as a consequence, indeed as a by-product of this process.

Previous concepts of the nature of spores have been based upon information, much of which is incomplete, and some definitely misleading. In the latter category, the theory that sporulation takes place in response to the stimulus of an unfavourable environment is so completely exploded as to require no further comment. But a less obvious misconception, arising from a failure to realise that more-or-less spore-like resting cells are of universal occurrence among bacteria, is the belief that spores are especially resistant to the processes of inanition, that is to say, of oxidation, which is the main cause of death in resting cells. Obviously spores are more resistant than the corresponding vegetative cells, but there is no evidence at all to suggest that they are more so than the resting cells of non-sporing bacteria ; and this is the true comparison. It is a commonplace of practical bacteriology that bacteria dried *in vacuo* will survive indefinitely.

This is a crucial point in the argument. If spores were more resistant than microcysts to inanition, then their possession would confer a most decided advantage, and no other explanation of their existence would be required. But the agencies to which spores are, in fact, especially resistant are most unlikely to be encountered under natural conditions, and, if they were, this resistance would confer little or no genetic advantage since the spore can neither metabolise nor reproduce. It may survive indefinitely in a hot spring, but evolve it cannot.

Previous theories have attempted to account for the spore in terms of its importance, not to the bacillus but to the bacteriologist, and the comparisons which have been made have not been true ones.

Whereas the aerobic genus *Bacillus* comprises a wide variety of specific types, retaining the relatively tiny spore, and capable of profiting by aerial distribution ; in the much smaller genus *Clostridium*, which by the genetic accident of anaerobiosis (perhaps associated with the habit of parasitism in the animal gut) has lost this opportunity, the spore itself is much larger. This is readily explicable as a retrogressive step in evolution, the loss of a character which has ceased to be of service, for which innumerable parallels could be cited from other fields. An analogous difference exists between *Streptomyces* and *Micromonospora*. The latter has adopted a thermophilic life in manure heaps and a semi-aquatic life in lake muds, and its spore is much less freely airborne than in the, probably less degenerate, *Streptomyces*. True *Actinomyces* and their sporogenous relatives may well be still more degenerate, parasitic descendants of freely-sporing ancestors.

The Gram-positive cocci resemble the sporing bacilli not only in their septate structure, but also in a high degree of adaptation to a terrestrial environment. The individual coccus is much reduced in size, and is not only capable of drifting in the dust like a spore, but, possibly because of a similar if less extreme concentration of the proteins, is among the most resistant of vegetative bacteria.

A parallel, but apparently independent line of evolution is found in the myxobacteria, of which the most highly evolved types are completely adapted to a terrestrial life. As already described, they are able to crawl upon moist surfaces, and their distribution is achieved by the enclosure of entire swarms in fruiting-bodies, often borne upon stalks to catch the air currents, which dry up and blow away in the wind.

F: RELATIONSHIPS OF AUTOTROPHIC BACTERIA
(3, 4)

Although inappropriate to detailed discussion in this book, it is an interesting confirmation of the validity of an evolutionary scheme for the classification of bacteria, such as has been outlined in this chapter, that the conclusions derivable from the parallel concept of progressive loss of synthetic power in the course of evolution are in excellent accordance with those based upon purely morphological reasoning.

This is well seen if the systematic relationships of the autotrophic bacteria are considered. Leaving aside those such as *Beggiatoa*, which are almost certainly not true bacteria, almost all autotrophs are either spirilla, vibrios, pseudomonads or those colonial pseudomonads some of which are classed as chlamydobacteria. They must therefore be regarded as primitive, aquatic forms ; which might reasonably be expected in any sound evolutionary system.

G : SUMMARY

There exists morphological evidence which suggests that the bacteria have evolved, in parallel with other groups of living organisms, from an aquatic to a terrestrial mode of life.

The most primitive bacteria are the spirilla, which have characters intermediate between those of typical bacteria and flagellates.

The most highly evolved bacteria are terrestrial and have special mechanisms for the aerial distribution of their resting stages. By the same criteria, the autotrophic bacteria are relatively primitive in respect of their morphology, as they appear to be in their physiology.

The evolutionary significance of different types of flagellation and of the bacterial endospore are discussed.

BIBLIOGRAPHY

(1) *Bergey's Manual of Determinative Bacteriology.* 6th ed. (1948) London : Ballière, Tindal & Cox.

(2) BISSET, K. A. (1950) Nature. 166. 431.

(3) BISSET, K. A. (1952) *Bacteria.* Edinburgh : Livingstone.

(4) BISSET, K. A. and GRACE, J. B. (1954) Symposium : " Autotrophic Microorganisms." Cambridge University Press.

(5) GRACE, J. B. (1954) J. Gen. Microbiol. 9. 325.

(6) KLUYVER, A. J. and VAN NIEL, C. B. (1936) Zbl. f. Bakt. II. 94. 369.

(7) PIJPER, A. (1946) J. Path. Bact. 58. 325.

(8) PRÉVOT, A. R. (1933) Ann. Sci. Nat. Bot., Sér. 10. 15. 23.

CHAPTER X

The Genetics of Bacteria

A: GENETICAL CONFIRMATION OF CYTOLOGY

(6, 8, 11, 12, 13, 14)

ANY organism which lives and reproduces its kind must possess a mechanism of inheritance, and there is no reason to believe that this mechanism in bacteria is different from that which is found in other living cells. The necessity for a linear arrangement of genes was emphasised by Lindegren in 1935, and shortly afterwards the short, chromosome-like body, whose existence he postulated, was described, or redescribed with great clarity by Stille (1937), Piekarski (1937), and Robinow (1942), so that its existence and nature have become generally recognised. After a period in which multiple or even branched chromosomes were postulated, for which there is no acceptable cytological evidence, the single chromosome has been genetically vindicated (Jinks, 1954).

Granted the existence of a chromosome-like body, it must be presumed that the genes which it carries are susceptible to the same hazards and chances of alteration or injury as the genes of other cells. Thus true, genetic mutation must be responsible, in bacteria as in other living organisms, for the appearance of permanent, heritable variation.

Such genetic evidence as is available supports the picture of the nuclear structure and sexual behaviour of bacteria which has been drawn in the previous pages of this book. In a review, Lederberg (1948) has stated : " The evidence suggests that this bacterium (*Bact. coli*) has a life-cycle comparable to *Zygosaccharomyces* : the vegetative cells are haploid (but not necessarily uninucleate) ; fertilisation is homothallic or unrestricted genetically ; the putative zygote undergoes immediate reduction without any intervening mitosis." To which it need only be added that this state of affairs is not peculiar to *Bact. coli*, but is common to most other bacteria for which evidence is available.

More recently Lederberg and his collaborators have produced evidence that vegetative diploid strains of *Bact. coli* may exist. The cells are longer than the haploids and have a larger number of similar nuclear elements.

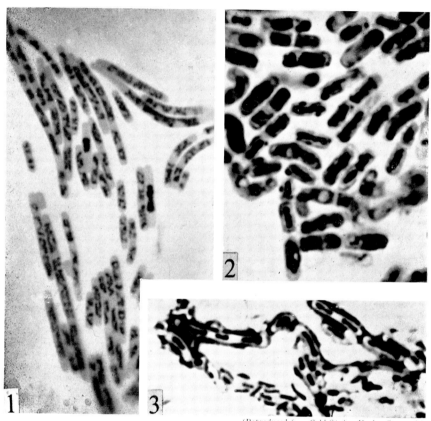

(Reproduced from Cold Spring Harbor Symposia).

Fig. 68

DIPLOID OR POLYPLOID FORMS OF NUCLEUS

(1) Cells of *Bacterium coli* known to be genetically diploid. (*By permission of Dr. J. Lederberg*).

(2) Presumed diploid or polyploid nuclei in post-fusion stages of a sporing bacillus.

(3) Secondary mycelium of *Streptomyces*.

In the sections dealing with the nature of the chromosome it has already been argued that the behaviour of the nuclear material at cell division indicates that all the nuclear units contained in the vegetative cell must be of equal value, that is, the cell is haploid but multinucleate. In sexual conjugation the two partners appear to be similar in status, and in bacteria of this type reduction occurs immediately after fusion. The status of the vegetative nucleus is also confirmed by the work of Witkin (1951), which is described in Chapter IV, Section G.

Some bacteria, such as sporing bacilli, streptomyces and the anaerobic actinomyces appear to have a prolonged diploid phase, and an examination of the genetical behaviour of such forms would greatly assist in the interpretation of their cytological appearances.

This correlation of conclusions between strictly genetical and strictly cytological studies gives grounds for increased confidence in both, and its importance cannot be too greatly stressed.

B: SOURCES OF GENETICAL EVIDENCE
(1, 2, 3, 4, 5, 6, 7, 9, 10, 15, 16)

The evidence upon which these genetical conclusions are based is mainly concerned with the nutritional requirements of the bacteria, that is to say, with their synthetic abilities. Problems of variation in resistance to disinfectants and to the bacteriophage have also been studied.

Gene recombination has been detected by the appearance of nutritionally unexacting " wild-type " strains of bacteria in mixed populations of nutritionally exacting mutants, and has been confirmed by a variety of ancillary experiments. The segregation and recombination of mutant characters shows interactions which may be regarded as indicative of linkage, and some evidence of the linear arrangement of genes has been obtained.

The comparative rarity of the recombination process gives reason for believing that conjugation must normally be autogamous, and only occasionally sexual. Here also the genetic and the cytological evidence are in agreement.

With bacteria, as with plants, animals and fungi, an increased mutation rate is induced by irradiation with ultra-violet light or X-rays. The mutation rate is proportional to the dosage, but is not related to the lethal effect. These mutations may become evident immediately after irradiation, or may appear only in the offspring of the treated cells ; presumably after conjugation.

The suggestion that hereditary factors in higher organisms may reproduce automatically in the cytoplasm of vegetative cells, independent of nuclear control, has its bacteriological parallel in the transformation of antigenic types of capsular material, in the pneumococcus. If a non-capsulated strain is brought into contact with a deoxyribose nucleic acid derived from a strain of different antigenic structure, it will commence to produce the capsular material appropriate to the strain from which the nucleic acid is derived, irrespective of the antigenic type of the capsule which it originally possessed. The genetic material, in this case, may be nuclear in origin, or may be the surface, secretory material of the cell, which is capable, as enzyme systems in other cells have been presumed to be capable, of reproducing itself without reference to the genetic constitution of the nucleus.

Mutations in the power of resistance to antibacterial agents, and in bacteriophage sensitivity, have both given evidence of a genetic system resembling that of higher organisms. There is, in fact, little to suggest that the entire, complex pattern of bacterial dissociation may not be explicable in terms of multiple and interrelated gene changes.

C: SUMMARY

The cytological evidence, presented in this work, is confirmed by genetical evidence.

BIBLIOGRAPHY

(1) AVERY, O. T. *et al.* (1944) J. Exp. Med. 79. 137.
(2) BEALE, G. H. (1948) J. Gen. Microbiol. 2. 131.
(3) BRAUN, W. (1953) Bacterial Genetics. Philadelphia. Saunders.
(4) BUNTING, M. I. (1946) Cold Spring Harbor Symposia. 11. 25.
(5) DEMEREC, M. and LATARJET, R. (1946) ibid. 11. 38.
(6) JINKS, J. L. (1954) Bacterial Genetics. Pers. Comm.
(7) LEDERBERG, J. (1947) Genetics. 32. 505.
(8) LEDERBERG, J. (1948) Heredity. 2. 145.
(9) LEDERBERG, J. and TATUM, E. L. (1946) Cold Spring Harbor Symposia. 11, 113.
(10) LEDERBERG, J., LEDERBERG, E. M., ZINDER, N. D., and LIVELY, E. R. (1951) Cold Spring Harbor Symposia. 16. 413.
(11) LINDEGREN, C. C. (1935) Zbl. f. Bakt. II. 92. 40.
(12) LURIA, S. E. (1947) Bact. Rev. 11. 1.
(13) MORRIS, E. O. (1951) J. Hyg., Camb. 49. 46.
(14) McCARTY, M., TAYLOR, H. E. and AVERY, O. T. (1946) Cold Spring Harbor Symposia. 11. 177.
(15) PIEKARSKI, G. (1937) Arch. f. Mikrobiol. 8. 428.
(16) ROBINOW, C. F. (1942) Proc. Roy. Soc. B. 130. 299.
(17) SCHRODINGER, E. (1944) What is Life ? Cambridge.
(18) STILLE, B. (1937) Arch. f. Mikrobiol. 8. 125.
(19) TATUM, E. L. and LEDERBERG, J. (1947) J. Bact. 53. 673.
(20) TAYLOR, H. E. (1949) Symposium : "The Nature of the Bacterial Surface," Soc. Gen. Microbiol. 61.
(21) WITKIN, E. M. (1951) Cold Spring Harbor Symposia. 16. 357.

Index

Printed in Great Britain
McLAGAN & CUMMING LTD., EDINBURGH